D0105475

# THE GEOGRAPHY OF EVOLUTION

COLLECTED ESSAYS

. . .

# THE GEOGRAPHY

GEORGE GAYLORD SIMPSON

# OF EVOLUTION

• • •

CHILTON BOOKS — Publishers

A Divison of Chilton Company

*Philadelphia & New York*

*First Edition*



Published in Philadelphia by Chilton Company
and simultaneously in Toronto, Canada,
by Ambassador Books, Ltd.

*Library of Congress Catalog Card Number 65-22541*

*Designed by ANNE CHURCHMAN*

Manufactured in the United States of America

# FOREWORD BY THE EDITOR

For the public interest, as well as for purely personal feelings of admiration, it is a deeply-felt pleasure to be able to bring this collection of Dr. Simpson's writings to the attention of a wider audience.

While the theme of the book is unified, the various essays, articles and lectures included herein are the result of the author's diverse activities, some being delivered abroad, as learned addresses, while others were written for scholarly journals in the United States.

But modern interest in evolution, and hence in zoology and paleontology as well, almost demands that these works, the products of the mind of one of our greatest living zoologists, should not be reserved for the exclusive use of advanced specialists in the sciences.

So clear and lucid is Dr. Simpson's style of writing and so cogent and compelling are his arguments and logic, that anyone literate can follow the fascinating story that he tells.

It is, of course, the story of life on our planet, and more specifically, the story of the vertebrates, the group of beings to which humanity belongs. No story is more worth telling, or more worth studying.

# PREFACE

It is a proper and, indeed, indispensable aim of biology to explain evolution in theoretical terms. Such explanation, in this as in any field of science, necessarily involves abstraction, with operations at one, two, or still more removes from the objective data. In considering theories of evolution, it nevertheless must be kept in mind that such theories, to have possible validity, must arise from and then in turn apply to real events, involving individual living things, occurring in a unique temporal sequence, and played out on and near the surface of a highly concrete body—our planet Earth.

This book gives first of all a brief review of evolutionary explanation, followed by an example of the gathering and codification of data: evidence of periodicity in the fossil record. Current problems of observation and interpretation bearing on evolution are then more broadly considered for the vertebrates, one of the animal groups most useful in this respect. The rest of the book, its greater part, is devoted to a class of evolutionary events and problems of outstanding importance and yet seldom sufficiently stressed in general texts or courses on evolution: that is, the geographic elements in evolution. Organisms (all those we know or are likely to) live on the earth; they differ from place to place; as populations, they move from place to place, even for thousands of miles. Their adaptions and their histories in general always involve geographic factors, and evolution cannot be sufficiently understood if those factors are neglected.

The seven parts making up this book have been selected and, although only slightly, modified so as to present a logical sequence treating the aforementioned themes. The parts were originally essays or lectures, prepared over a period of years and published separately in widely scattered and in some instances rather inaccessible places. None has hitherto been included in book publication, and it is hoped that their collection in this form will be a convenience and will make them accessible to a wider audience.

GEORGE GAYLORD SIMPSON

July, 1965
Los Pinavetes, La Jara,
New Mexico

# ACKNOWLEDGEMENTS

Most of the essays appearing in this collection have appeared previously (and in a few cases appear here with slight changes). Grateful acknowledgement is made to the publications and societies listed below for the use of articles previously published by them.

"Evolution and the History of Life" . . . *Bulletin of the Wagner Free Institute of Science,* vol. 25, No. 2, May 1950.

"Periodicity in Vertebrate Evolution" . . . *The Distribution of Evolutionary Explosions in Geologic Time* (symposium). Published by *The Journal of Paleontology,* vol. 26, No. 3, May 1952.

"Some Problems of Vertebrate Paleontology" . . . *Science,* vol. 133, No. 3465, May 26, 1961.

"Evolution and Geography" . . . published in 1953 as a Condon Lecture by the Oregon State System of Higher Education.

"Historical Zoogeography of Australian Mammals" . . . *Evolution,* vol. 15, No. 4, Dec. 30, 1961.

"History of the Fauna of Latin America . . . *Science in Progress* (Seventh Series), Yale University Press, 1951.

"Mammalian Evolution on the Southern Continents" was a paper prepared for the XVI International Congress of Zoology in Washington, D.C. An abstract was published in the *Proceedings* of the Congress, vol. 4, Aug. 1963.

• ● ●

# CONTENTS

# THE GEOGRAPHY OF EVOLUTION

# PART 1

*The introductory essay is a broad explanation of current evolutionary theory. The course of studies in evolution, a brief outline of the organization of life into groups, and a survey of what evolution* means, *make up the body of the work. But what evolutionary theory is* not, *and cannot be, and the blind alleys of evolutionary science, are also analyzed.*

# Evolution and the History of Life

## TIME AND LIFE

Life may be studied in many different ways, and biology, the science of life, tends to split up into numerous specialties. Systematics, ecology, biogeography, cytology, biochemistry, physiology, genetics, paleontology, comparative anatomy, experimental embryology, and many other biological subjects are now sharply distinct fields, each with its specialized researchers and each, indeed, further subdivided because each has become too rich and complex for one student to retain all its details. There are, nevertheless, general principles basic to any study of life and the most important of such principles is that life has a history; it has evolved. All fields of biology can profitably be examined from the historical point of view. All have data to contribute to the study of evolution and all are in turn illumined by knowledge of evolution.

Studying life from a historical point of view means giving special attention to the element of time. All dynamic studies of life processes involve time. Processes produce changes and changes occur in time. (Even instantaneous changes have reference to *before* and *after.*) The time scale of many biological studies is severely restricted. Reliable observations of living nature cover, at most, a few hundred years and are usually still more stringently limited. Laboratory experiments usually cover a few hours or days, at most a few years. The history of life involves a far longer time scale, the scale of geological time. The age of the earth is now known to be well over 3,000,000,000 years. Life has been in existence for at least two-thirds of that span.

All biological studies have a bearing on the history of life, but fossils are contemporaneous records of that history and paleontology is the science that studies it directly and at firsthand. The earliest part of the fossil record is exceedingly poor and fragmentary. A relatively good and continuous record begins with the Cambrian period, about 600,000,000 years ago. On this long-time scale, events that take on the order of hundreds of thousands of years and upward can usually be readily followed in sequence. Events lasting on the order of tens of thousands of years and less usually cannot at present be followed clearly. That is, they are so rapid as often to appear instantaneous with the present refinement of methods. On the long-time scale we are, then, studying mainly the results of processes that are exceedingly slow in terms of human life or experimentation.

Many of the crucial processes of evolution, such as the origin of a new species, seem in fact to be very slow as they occur in nature; so slow that the changes involved would appear to be zero on the short-time scale of laboratory study. Some students have suggested that short-scale effects seen in experimentation are not important in the long scale of earth history. What happens to a billion rats in ten million years may not be explicable by multiplying from what happens to a thousand rats in ten years. One of the great contributions of paleontology is in checking theoretical results of experimentation to see whether they really do apply to the greater and more important sequence of evolution in nature. There are also numerous essential factors of evolution that cannot be studied in the laboratory at all because they demand the longer-time scale. Rates of evolution in nature are usually too slow for the shorter scale. Dynamic study of the broad patterns of evolution also requires the longer scale. Above all, the most fundamental changes in the course of evolution, the origin of basically new sorts of plants and animals, can be determined only with reference to the long-time scale.

The fossil record is incomplete and must always remain so, but it is very rich from the Cambrian period onward and intensive modern collecting is still rapidly adding to it. In the classification of animals, conservative zoologists recognize about twenty major groups—each representing a really basic type or grade of organization—called "phyla." About half of them have left no fossil record, or so little that study reveals nothing of particular value. Most of these are, however, rare and unimportant groups whose status as basic types perhaps would not be maintained if we *did* know their history. Most of the phyla of real and established importance have fairly good fossil records. These phyla include the Protozoa (one-celled or undivided animals such as the amoeba), Porifera (sponges), Coelenterata (corals and their relatives), Bryozoa ("moss animals"), Brachiopoda (lamp shells), Echinodermata (starfish, sea urchins, and others), Mollusca (clams, snails, and most of the other shelled animals and some nonshelled allies), Arthropoda (crabs, scorpions, spiders, insects, and others), and Chordata or Vertebrata (fishes, amphibians, reptiles, birds, and mammals).

The record shows that all these phyla have changed in variety and abundance at various times. The very simplest of them, such as the protozoans and the sponges, probably are older than the others, although as a matter of fact present knowledge of the fossil record does not definitely substantiate this. Most of the phyla do not represent a progression, one from the other, but appear in the record, and perhaps really arose, at about the same time around the beginning of the Paleozoic era, perhaps 500 to 700 million years ago. Of course the span of about 200 million years involved here is also a very long time, but it is less than a tenth of the whole history of life. As far as has been determined, no new phyla have appeared during the last several hundred million years. Still more striking is the fact that no phylum clearly worthy of that rank is known ever to have become extinct.

Within each phylum there have been many changes. New groups constantly arise and they tend either to develop new ways of life, extending the range occupied by the phylum, or to replace older types within the range already occupied. A transformation in anatomy and in physiology usually accompanies or precedes the expansion or replacement. Among vertebrates, several different major groups of primarily aquatic forms, all popularly called fishes, arose successively. From one of these groups amphibians arose and started extending the vertebrate domain from water to land. Reptiles later carried this extension further, and largely, but not completely, replaced the amphibians. Some reptiles were transformed to mammals, which eventually rose to dominance on the land. Others were transformed to birds and developed a new, large domain.

## PRINCIPLES AND PROCESSES IN THE HISTORY OF LIFE

The fossil record reveals what sorts of organisms have lived at particular successive times in the course of earth history and where they lived on the face of the earth. This factual record is only the first step in the historical study of evolution. The next step is to try to get at the processes underlying the observed sequences and to understand the general principles involved.

Earlier generations of students tried to infer from the record a system of natural laws governing evolution. In the physical sciences a number of rules had been discovered, usually mathematical in formulation, which seemed *always* to be followed and which greatly simplified comprehension and use of mechanical and chemical things. Such laws are, for instance, the law of gravity or the law of combining weights. Many biologists assumed that evolution was a similarly lawful process and that its laws were implicit in the historical record.

Unfortunately, the "laws" of evolution have turned out not to be laws at all in the same sense that physical and chemical rules are laws. Organisms are subject to laws of that sort, but their history is not. In spite of the popular saying, history does not repeat itself, and historical "laws" are of quite a different sort. The "laws" of history are generalized descriptions as to what has often happened under more or less similar circumstances. There are always exceptions, if only because historical circumstances are never twice exactly the same. Much misinterpretation of the course of evolution has resulted from failure to recognize that this is history and that its interpretation involves historical principles rather than, or in addition to, physical laws.

The basic facts of evolution and the basic interpretations of the record concern the relationships of organisms, their phylogeny or descent one from another in different and often branching lines. It is only after these lines of descent have been inferred that it becomes possible to seek for historical generalizations about evolution.

One of the most striking things about phylogenies as worked out from the fossil record and from their present-day results is that they frequently diverge in multiple lines. Starting with a common ancestry, different descendants may become adapted to widely different habits and habitats. This phenomenon has been called "adaptive radiation." It may take place on a large scale, as in the case of the placental mammals, for instance, which all started as small shrewlike creatures and have adaptively radiated into such diverse types as bats, armadillos, rats, whales, cats, cows, men, and a thousand others. It may also take place on a small scale, for example in the case of "Darwin's finches" in the Galápagos Islands, all clearly similar and related birds but with some variety of habits and corresponding structural differences.

Adaptive radiation is most striking when some group reaches a new region or a new basic structural type, making available to it a variety of adaptations. The process may then be widespread and rapid in terms of evolutionary history—that is, it may reach considerable proportions in only a few million years. This sort of event is commonly called "explosive" or "eruptive" evolution. In a broader sense, adaptive radiation is the main process by which animals have become increasingly diverse in the course of history.

Another sort of diversity, one that is indeed usually involved in the beginning of adaptive radiation, arises from geographic isolation. Animals in different regions, prevented from crossbreeding, tend to become different, and finally are so distinct that interbreeding is impossible even if they do meet. Adaptive radiation may occur separately in two different regions. If similar ways of life are possible in both regions, it frequently happens that different lines of descent become adapted in similar ways. They are then likely to develop special functional and structural resemblances to each other. If the two lines involved were similar to begin with (hence near their common ancestry and rather closely related), they continue to be similar as they evolve, and this phenomenon is called parallelism. If they were more distinct to begin with (farther from a common ancestry and less closely related), they become more similar as they acquire similar adaptations, and this is called convergence. As an example, South America during the tens of millions of years while it was an island continent was the scene of a great adaptive radiation among mammals, many of which converged toward forms separately evolving in North America.

Parallelism and convergence intergrade and are not always sharply distinguishable. Parallelism tends to involve closer resemblances than convergence, but neither process is known ever to result in identity. Once truly separate lines of descent have arisen, they seem never to become precisely the same again. In history *everything* that has happened earlier is the cause of what follows. This total cause is added to at every moment and cannot be the same at any two times, so that the results cannot be exactly the same. The past is irrevocable and history is irreversible. This is the real basis for the "law" of the irreversibility of evolution, often called "Dollo's Law" after a famous Belgian paleontologist, although in fact the American paleontologist Scott, and perhaps others, had discovered this "law" before Dollo.

Because this principle does reflect an inherent characteristic of history, it is more general and in that sense nearer to being a true law than are most of the "laws" of evolution. It is strictly true, however, only as regards *exact* repetition. In dealing with similarities, rather than identities, correct understanding of the principle means only that reversal is often more or less improbable. As regards particular characters, reversal may not be improbable. Remote ancestors of the whales were fishes although closer ancestors were four-footed land mammals. Whales became fishlike in many respects by convergence toward fishes, and their fishlike characters were reversals of evolution. But they did not become fishes. Their oxygen intake, for instance, continued to be by lungs, as in their land-living ancestors, and not by gills, as in fishes.

Misapplication of the principle of irreversiblity has sometimes falsified phylogeny. It has been supposed, for example, that once animals or parts of them had become large, they could not become smaller again; so that large Ice Age bison could not be ancestral to the smaller bison of today, or cats with enlarged canines to those with smaller canines. We now know many examples of reversion of this sort and know that these were incorrect applications of the principle, which is, nevertheless, valid when it is expressed only as a probability and with understood limitations.

Other generalizations refer to the sorts of changes that are likely to occur in the evolution of various groups. An example is the principle that there is likely to be a progressive reduction in number of parts but that those remaining are likely to become more specialized in function. For instance, early relatives of the crustaceans had many legs, all almost alike, while modern crabs have comparatively few legs, some of them quite different from the others. This is frequently called "Williston's Law," although Stromer claims that it should be "Stromer's Law," and earlier claimants could probably be found if it were worth while to search. Of course this "law" has numerous exceptions, and it is not really a law at all but a generalization as to what has often happened.

The concept that the historical course of evolution is rigidly determined by a set of simple and universal natural laws reached its height in the theory of orthogenesis. Descriptively, orthogenesis is applied to cases in which evolutionary change tends to continue in the same direction for a long time, or until extinction of the group. As a matter of fact such a tendency is certainly not universal, and many paleontologists (including me) now think that it is unusual, that this "rule" is the exception. Support for it is either erroneous, as can be exemplified by the plainly nonorthogenetic evolution of the horse family, often cited as orthogenetic, or is based on trying to make the facts fit the rule, refusing to accept the reality of phylogenies that are not orthogenetic. Evolution does commonly have trends and it is not, in general, random. This more limited and flexible orientation is real, but the rigid rectilinearity ascribed to evolution by the theory of orthogenesis probably is not.

Orthogenesis has often been taken not only as generalized description but also as an attempted explanation, according to which evolutionary trends are not guided by natural selection or other factors in interaction between organism and environment but by vital forces wholly internal to the organism or by an urge toward a metaphysically determined goal. The phenomena of trends, or of orthogenesis to the extent that it may exist, are thus crucial in consideration of the major explanatory theories of evolution, to be considered next.

## EXPLANATIONS OF EVOLUTION

Description of what has happened in the course of evolution, and historical principles that generalize aspects of that description, still are not explanations of evolution. They are among the materials or the evidence on which an explanation must be based. Explanation must also call, and perhaps in still greater degree, on all other sorts of biological studies. One of the essential contributions of more strictly historical studies is to check on evolutionary processes suggested by laboratory and field observations, to determine whether these processes can in fact account for what has occurred in the history of life.

As regards details, innumerable different theories of evolution have been advanced, but these fall into a few broad schools of thought, one of which is now decidedly predominant among the best-informed special students of the subject. The most fundamental cleavage among evolutionary theories is between those that are vitalistic and those that are materialistic. The vitalists maintain that evolution is strongly influenced, if not wholly guided, by nonmaterial factors, that life involves an essence, a vital principle, an intrinsic something that is different in kind from anything present in the nonliving physical universe. The materialists of course recognize the obvious fact that living matter behaves differently from nonliving, but they maintain that the difference arises from vital organization only, and that the substances and operations involved in this characteristic and complex organization are the same as those of the material universe in general.

The vitalist arguments are mainly the negative claim that evolutionary phenomena, particularly those of adaptation, *cannot* be explained in materialistic terms and the positive claim that some phenomena, especially orthogenesis, *must* correspond with the action of an innate, or nonmaterial, driving force. In both respects, the factual evidence adduced is in part demonstrably erroneous, as was suggested previously for orthogenesis in this sense. Such sound evidence as is given usually boils down to demonstration that evolution is not a *wholly* random process. The vitalistic conclusion does not really follow from this, because no current materialistic theory suggests that evolution is wholly random and there are evident and demonstrable nonrandom material factors in evolution. On the other hand, it seems clear that evolution is *partly* random, which is embarrassing for most vitalistic theories.

There are a few vitalists among competent students of evolution, especially in Europe, but an overwhelming majority in Europe as well as elsewhere are materialists. In the United States this is true to such an extent that most are inclined to consider the vitalist-materialist controversy a dead issue. This statement applies, however, only to the specialized technical students of evolution. Many philosophers, some nonbiological scientists, and perhaps a majority of such laymen as have ideas on the subject, are vitalists. The great appeal of vitalism to those poorly qualified to judge the issue was attested by the remarkable popular success of Du Noüy's *Human*

*Destiny* and more recently of Teilhard's *Phenomenon of Man.* Those works are both vitalistic and finalistic, adding to the usual vitalistic thesis the idea of purpose in evolution, of a goal toward which the history of life has tended under divine guidance. The popularity of the theory in the face of its rejection by most specialists is clearly due to wishful thinking and prejudice, not to scientific merit.

Two main materialistic theories of evolution predominated during the latter part of the nineteenth century: Neo-Lamarckism and Darwinism, which developed into Neo-Darwinism as the argument between the two schools progressed. The Neo-Lamarckians ascribed evolutionary changes in organisms to the inheritance of modifications acquired during their lifetimes as a result of their activities and of environmental influences. Darwin, working before any effective knowledge of the mechanism of heredity had been achieved, accepted such inheritance as real, but he showed that it cannot be more than a subsidiary part of the evolutionary process, which also requires some other and more general cause. This objection to the Neo-Larmarckian factor has been emphasized by later work, and the whole theory was finally decisively overthrown when increased knowledge of heredity showed that the inheritance of acquired characters, as such, does not occur.

Testing of the theory was so exhaustive and the results were so conclusively opposed to it that Neo-Lamarckism had become a dead issue to almost all well-informed evolutionists until its amazing revival as "Michurinism" in the Soviet Union by reactionary and incompetent but politically powerful biologists and officials.* Since evolutionary biology in Russia must be labeled "Darwinian" to be ideologically acceptable, Michurinism has been duly represented as Darwinian on the grounds that Darwin did accept the inheritance of acquired characters. In fact, Darwin considered this factor as wholly secondary in importance and his belief that it had any role is among the few of his opinions that must now be considered definitely incorrect. It is a scientific step backward to

* It seems now to be discredited there as well.

revive Neo-Lamarckism and it is terminological trickery to dub it Darwinian.

Neo-Darwinism resembled Neo-Lamarckism not only in being materialistic but also in seeking causes of evolution in the interaction of organism and environment. Neo-Darwinians were truly Darwinian and differed from Neo-Lamarckians in designating natural selection as the crucial point in this interaction. It is the nonrandom material factor that refutes the vitalist insistence that Darwinism is evolution by chance. Natural selection can only operate on hereditary variation and the source of such variation and the laws (properly such) of its transmission were unknown to Darwin or his 19th-century followers. This was the principal really serious defect in their theory.

The missing element in Neo-Darwinism was supplied by the development of the modern science of genetics. An early result was a school of mutationist or DeVriesian evolutionary theory in which natural selection or the organism-environment interaction in general was minimized. Evolution was considered an essentially random process, at least as far as concerned its orientation toward adaptation, which is a crucial point in all evolutionary theories. Adaptation was supposed to arise by chance or by preadaptation, defined as the appearance of mutant forms that happened to be adapted to an available way of life.

More mature reflection made this theory untenable in its original austerity. The vitalists, the Neo-Darwinians, and the Neo-Lamarckians, so basically at odds in other respects, did agree that there is an essential nonrandom element in evolution, and their evidence was and is overwhelmingly convincing. The answer to what thus became a dilemma was found in, essentially, a synthesis of Neo-Darwinism and mutationist theory. The resulting modern synthetic theory is too complex to summarize briefly in accordance with the great real complexity of the course of evolution. The central idea is, however, the rather simple concept that the materials of evolution arise by mutations of various sorts and other processes of heredity, while the integration of these materials into functional, adapted organisms and their creative channeling in the historical flow of life are performed by natural selection. Natural selection is now usually viewed more broadly than by Darwin's immediate followers and is defined as any consistent trend in differential reproduction.

This general theory is now supported by an imposing array of paleontologists, geneticists, and other biological specialists. Differences of opinion on relatively minor points naturally persist and many details remain to be filled in, but the essentials of the explanation of the history of life have probably now been achieved.

• ● ●

# PART 2

*The second essay treats of the changes which have taken place in the vertebrate subphylum and, in more detail, the chronology of those changes over hundreds of millions of years. The rates of appearance and disappearance of the various vertebrate orders, families, and genera are analyzed and related to the geology and climate of the Earth.*

# Periodicity in Vertebrate Evolution

Search for *the* cause of evolution has been abandoned. It is now clear that evolution has no single or simple cause. Its process is a continuous flux in which the total situation of any instant is the result of all previous changes and the cause of all that follow. This total situation includes the physical environment, all the biological elements of ecological associations, and an intricate complex of genetic, associative, and other factors within each of the evolving population groups. In the broad constellation of conditions determining the course of evolution, changes in physical environment necessarily change the total situation, and they are therefore necessarily accompanied or followed by some sort of evolutionary change. This relationship is firmly established and is not here under dispute. The precise nature of the relationship, its effect on the broadest or most basic episodes in evolution, and its possibly periodic recurrence are, however, still in need of discussion.

This study was originally prepared for a symposium whose purpose was to determine, first, whether there are periodic, general, essentially world-wide times of intensified evolutionary activity and, second, whether these correspond with similarly general and periodic increases in diastrophism—evolutionary events in the physical history of the earth's crust. The intention is to test a possible causal relationship, existence of which has commonly been taken for granted and is widely taught as fact to students of historical geology. The dogma has, however, been repeatedly questioned both on the biological and on the physical side. The choice of the topic for this symposium showed that doubts exist as to the validity of earlier conclusions on this subject.

This particular contribution is concerned with the biological aspect, only, of the problem and with the evidence of a single phylum of animals, the Vertebrata. The data for this phylum, although obviously incomplete, are exceptionally good both in the abundance of paleontological records and in the progress that has been made in their compilation and interpretation. The present aim is to summarize some of these data in such a way as to bring out any periodicity or other regularities that may exist in episodes of proliferation and of extinction among vertebrates. Discussion will then bear on the possible evolutionary significance of such regularities as are found and on their possible correlation with events in earth history.

## DATA

The problem involves origins, increases, decreases, and extinctions of groups of vertebrates. The data are records of occurrence of the various taxonomic entities within each period (or, as may be practicable, epoch or age). Strictly speaking, the factual data do not include times of origin or of extinction, but only the times of first and last appearance in the record as known. These times of appearance certainly do not correspond precisely with real origins and extinctions, nor can the recorded increases and decreases be taken as accurately proportional to those that really occurred. In the present summary it is unnecessary to enumerate or evaluate the numerous sources of error, although these have been carefully considered and allowance has been made for them in deductions

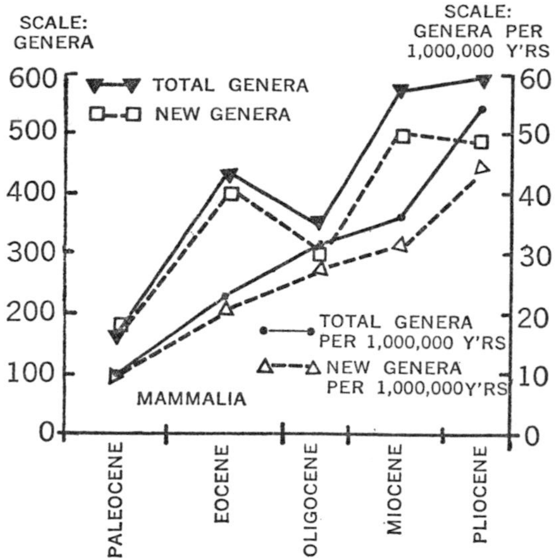


Fig. 1. Graphs of numbers of known genera and of new genera (or first appearances) of mammals in the epochs of the Tertiary.

from the record. The data are taken as they are. First appearances in the known record are accepted as more nearly objective and basic than opinions as to the time when each group really originated.

The record thus compiled is clearly not random, as will appear below. It has a large measure of regularity and consistency that seems to attest correspondence with real events. In particular, well-marked trends of increase or decrease seem, with some exceptions and when taken broadly, to be significant even though they cannot furnish a precise measurement of the real rates. Sharply delimited highs and lows in recorded frequencies seem, with similar exceptions and precautions, to correspond closely with times of real maxima and minima in proliferation of the groups in question.

Data were compiled for the most part from Romer (1945), with some additions and modifications especially as concerns mam-

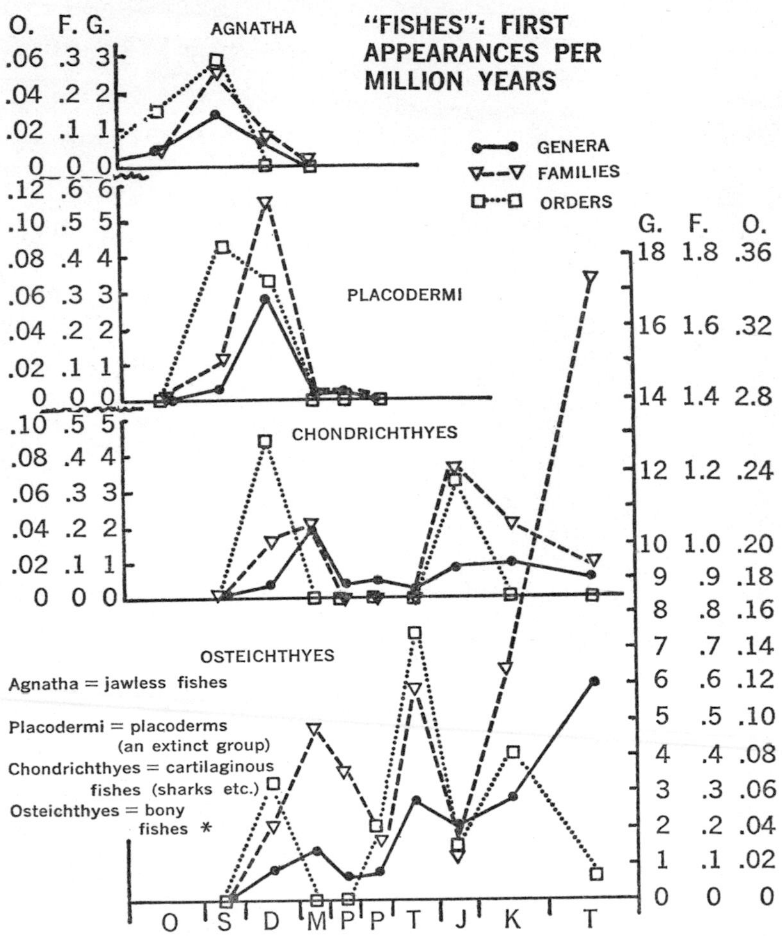


Fig. 2. Graphs of first appearances per million years of known orders, families, and genera of the four classes of "fishes." O., F., and G. above the scales stand for orders, families and genera per million years. The time scale at the bottom has symbols for the geological periods as follows: Ordovician, Silurian, Devonian, Mississippian, Pennsylvanian, Permian, Triassic, Jurassic, Cretaceous, Tertiary.

* Like other technical names, these do not necessarily describe all the included animals correctly. Some Chondrichthyes have bones, and some Osteichthyes do not.

mals. The basic compilation (assisted by Nathan Altshuler) was made as part of a larger project to survey some numerical aspects of the whole fossil record of animals, jointly with Norman D. Newell and assisted by numerous other specialists. Here such data as seem to bear most closely on this particular problem are summarily presented in the form of graphs, only.

The numerical data consist of a census for various taxonomic categories known for various times in the geological record. Analysis of numbers of species was not attempted because of factors, relating mainly to sampling and to subjectivity, that make inferences from them excessively unreliable. Within the Vertebrata, records of orders and genera are most useful. Records of families have also been compiled and are included in some of the present graphs (Figs. 2, 3), but in general they add little to what is shown by the orders and genera. For each time and for each selected taxonomic level, figures in the tabulations (not here published as such) include total numbers, first appearances, last appearances, and continuations from preceding times. For the particular subject of this essay, first appearances are most significant because interest is focused mainly on times of maximum proliferation or episodes of so-called "explosive" evolution. It is also true that the total numbers, especially for genera, usually closely follow the general trends for numbers of first appearances, as can be seen in Fig. 1. Some broad data on last appearances (Fig. 5) and on totals and survivals (Fig. 6) are given, but emphasis is here on first appearances.

Numbers of known taxonomic units are given by periods and not by shorter time units except for mammals, which are in some graphs (Figs. 1, 3) tabulated by epochs in the Tertiary. Some allowance must be made for the fact that the long time units, although useful for purposes of broad summary, conceal some important details. Similar allowance is necessary for the conventionalization of placing each record at the middle of the corresponding time unit.

Even if the exceedingly short Quaternary period is omitted, the lengths of the geological periods or epochs differ by a factor of at least 3 to 1. (Few geologists will question that the Cambrian was three times as long as the Mississippian, for instance, or that the Eocene was about twice as long as the Oligocene.) With a constant rate of proliferation, the graphed values of first appearances would be much higher for a long period than for a short period. The fact that the lengths of the periods are not accurately established introduces another uncertain and subjective element, but comparability is better if allowance is made for variations in these lengths. In most of the graphs (Figs. 2–5), this is done by showing, not the total count for each period, but this count divided by the assumed length of the period in millions of years. This usually does, in fact, produce smoother and apparently more consistent graphs, as shown by the example of Fig. 1. The time scale at the bottom of each graph shows the relative assumed lengths of the periods.

The fossil record of the birds, which is still very poor, involves so many adventitious irregularities and would require so much inference and discussion that it is omitted here. Such as it is, this record (which has also been compiled and graphed but not published) is not inconsistent with conclusions drawn from other, better data for vertebrates as a whole. For all the groups, Pleistocene and Recent records are omitted, because the very different sampling conditions for those epochs would require lengthy discussion and adjustment of the data.

## PEAKS OF RATES OF FIRST APPEARANCE

The curves of first appearance per million years for seven classes of vertebrates (Figs. 2, 3) show certain characteristics common to all or most of these classes. Each curve, whether for orders, families, or genera, rises to a relatively early peak, generally in the period of first appearance of the class or in the following period. Only for the family and generic curves of the Amphibia is the first peak as late as the second period after that of the first appearance of the class. Mesozoic mammals are so poorly known that the reality of the low, recorded Jurassic peaks may be questioned, but better knowledge is more likely to emphasize these peaks than to eliminate them. Each curve tends to fall off rather rapidly from this first peak. In the period following the peak, there is a significant drop in almost every case. The only noteworthy exceptions to this are the ordinal and family curves for reptiles, which maintain the peak level for two and three geologic periods, respectively. Some, but as yet insufficient, further analysis strongly suggests that this apparently exceptional feature in the reptilian record is an artifact caused by the coarseness of the time scale for the present graphs. If scaled to epochs or ages, it is highly probable that there was a

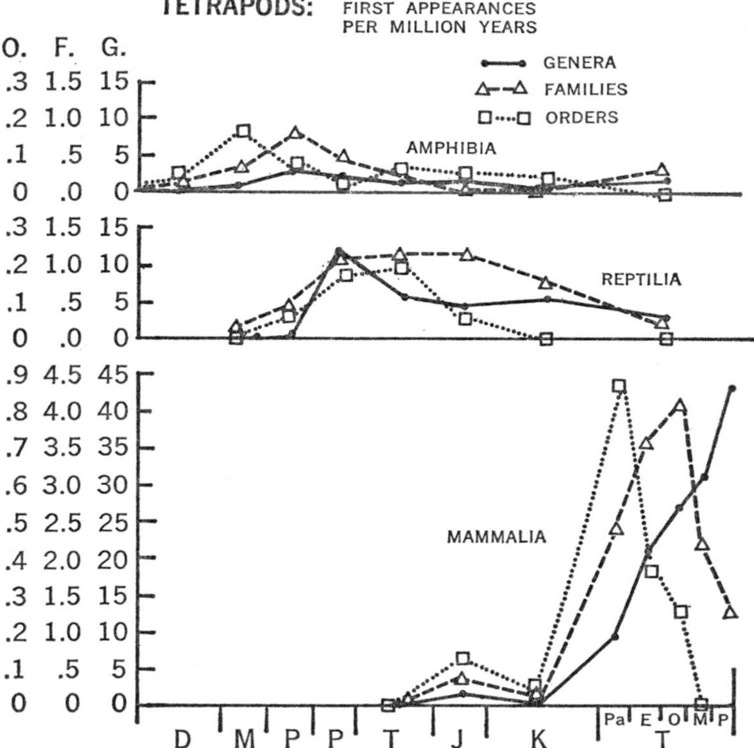


Fig. 3. Graphs of first appearances of three classes of tetrapods. Method of construction and abbreviations as in Fig. 2, with addition of the Tertiary epochs to the time scale for the Mammalia.

drop in rate after the Permian peaks and that the apparent continuation of those peaks in the Triassic represents, in fact, a new rise in each curve. The reality of the Cretaceous drop in the mammalian curves is open to considerable question, yet this does agree with the usual trend of the other curves.

After the first peaks, the curves for the two earliest and most primitive classes decline more or less steadily to extinction (Placodermi) or near it (Agnatha, with a few living relicts but no fossil record after the Devonian). The Chondrichthyes have a clear-cut second peak on all three curves, and the Osteichthyes have not only a second but also a third peak. The Amphibia have slight but probably real second peaks for orders and for genera. There is no second peak in the present graphs for the Reptilia, but (as noted above) this is probably an artifact and second peaks probably did occur at each taxonomic level during the Mesozoic. If the Jurassic peak for mammals is real, then their very sharp and unquestionably real Tertiary peaks are to be considered second peaks.

Omitting the dubious first (?) mammalian and second (?) reptilian peaks, the distribution by periods is as follows:

| | *Ordinal Peaks* | *Family Peaks* | *Generic Peaks* |
|---|---|---|---|
| TERTIARY | Mammalia (2?) | Osteichthyes 3<br>Mammalia (2?) | Osteichthyes 3<br>Mammalia (2?) |
| CRETACEOUS | Osteichthyes 3 | | Chondrichthyes 2 |
| JURASSIC | Chondrichthyes 2 | Chondrichthyes 2 | (Amphibia 2?) |
| TRIASSIC | Osteichthyes 2<br>Amphibia (2?) | Osteichthyes 2 | Osteichthyes 2 |
| PERMIAN | Reptilia 1 | Reptilia 1 | Reptilia 1 |
| PENNSYLVANIAN | | Amphibia 1 | Amphibia 1 |
| MISSISSIPPIAN | Amphibia 1 | Chondrichthyes 1<br>Osteichthyes 1 | Chondrichthyes 1<br>Osteichthyes 1 |
| | Chondrichthyes 1<br>Osteichthyes 1 | Placodermi | Placodermi |
| SILURIAN | Agnatha<br>Placodermi | Agnatha | Agnatha |

 


The spaces are almost completely filled. In *every* period after that in which the phylum first appears (Ordovician), some class of vertebrates was in a phase of markedly rapid proliferation of new groups. Moreover this is true for each of the three taxonomic levels graphed except for orders in the Pennsylvanian and families in the Cretaceous. The apparent exceptions have little or no significance. A *class* of vertebrates (Reptilia) first appeared in the Pennsylvanian, and rates of appearance of new families were high in the Cretaceous (for Chondrichthyes, Osteichthyes, and Reptilia) even though still higher rates in adjacent periods keep these from appearing as peaks on the broadly generalized curves of the present graphs.

Thus, in the words of the original proposal for this symposium by L. G. Henbest, *within* a single class (and the same is true for smaller subdivisions not here graphed) there is definitely a tendency for "proliferations . . . to be segregated in particular epochs." As between different groups or for the Vertebrata as a whole, however, there is certainly no tendency for their times of most rapid diversification to coincide. The various segregated times of proliferation for each class or lesser group are so scattered through geologic time that one or more occurs in every period pertinent to this history. In this sense, "the proliferations are not segregated but are distributed more or less evenly through time."

This distribution of peaks of differentiation of new groups through time is more or less even, but it is not random. There are evident systematic relationships between the various peaks. Possible interpretations of this fact require further discussion, which follows on later pages.

## SEQUENCE OF ORDINAL, FAMILY, AND GENERIC PEAKS

Within each class, there is a strong tendency for rates of appearance of new genera to rise and fall in the same sequence as the rates for orders, but to do so at later times. In the ten most clear-cut peaks seen in the graphs (Figs. 2, 3) a generic peak occurs one period later than the ordinal peak in six cases. The four apparent exceptions, which have ordinal and generic peaks in the same period, are probably not really such in any case but are artifacts of the presentation on a coarse time scale. In each case the generic peak was probably later than the ordinal peak by a considerable time and yet occurred in the same period. This is positively established for the Mammalia and is very clearly shown in the graph of epochs (Fig. 3, bottom) rather than by periods. Ordinal and generic peaks occur in the same period, the Tertiary, but the former in the Paleocene and the latter in the Pliocene, with an interval of at least 45 million years between them.

The evidence is that a generic peak regularly (usually, and perhaps always) occurs some 25 to 50 million years after an ordinal peak. In the case of the mammals, graphed with a more refined time scale, the family peak falls between those for orders and for genera, as might be expected. On the period scale, the family curve tends to parallel the generic rather closely and simultaneously. This perhaps reflects the classifier's frequent habit of treating a family simply as a bundle of genera, so that more genera automatically mean more families, whereas the number of orders recognized is largely independent of the number of genera. However that may be, further consideration of families can add little to conclusions from the relationships of appearance rates in orders or genera.

As vertebrate classification has been worked out and is reflected in these data, large categories such as orders represent basic and new adaptive types. Lines of descent from these normally diverge and involve adaptive radiation, but within the scope or building on the basis of the ancestral ordinal type. Families, genera, and other lower taxonomic units categorize the lesser adaptive types. They also include the many more or less adventitiously isolated groups, which reduplicate a type in a variety of localities and environments and which fill in many ecological niches within broadly similar life zones. The vertebrate record shows that the peak of splitting into basic types, as exemplified in rate of appearance of new orders, considerably precedes the similar peak of splitting into lesser groups, such as genera. When genera are appearing at their highest rate, the rate of appearance of orders is dropping rapidly. As regards total numbers of taxonomic units, also, in a given group (as a rule) when the number of orders is highest, the number of genera is lower than it later becomes. Past the ordinal peak, the number of orders tends to decrease as the number of genera increases.

Now, in studying the supposed phenomenon of "explosive" evolution and testing possible correlation of this with physical events, when does the "explosion" occur? By definition, the "explosion" is a relatively abrupt increase in numbers of taxonomic units, or in their rate of appearance. In absolute numbers, genera and species are most numerous and they are also at the level of usual taxonomic study. The "explosion" is commonly taken to be an increase at this level. But peaks of incidence of new genera follow those of new orders with such regularity in the record here presented that it seems inescapable that the fundamental events, in some sense the cause of the expansion, is the earlier ordinal differentiation. Then seeming correlation of generic "explosion" with contemporaneous physical events would appear to be purely adventitious, because the generic expansion was the outcome of events of some 25 or 50 million years earlier.

In fact, it becomes impossible to pin down the essential point of this chain to any particular expansive phase in it. A most fundamental adaptive type categorized as a class appears, and in 25 to 50 million years its rate of ordinal differentiation reaches an "explosive climax." In another 25 or 50 million years the rate of generic differentiation reaches a similar but quite distinct climax. The whole process seems to be a biological, evolutionary sequence affecting all vertebrates throughout the history of the group. It naturally occurs against the background and within the limitations of the physical environment, but it seems impossible even to make a start at realistic correlation of so regular and continuous a process with intermittent tectonic episodes. The occurrences of second and third climaxes within a given class fall into exactly the same sort of sequence, for without exception they also are initiated by emergence of new adaptive or structural types which simply do not happen, in our classifications, to be formalized at the rank of classes. Once they arise, a sequence of ordinal and generic highs follows in due course as it did after the class as a whole arose.

The second peaks of the Chondrichthyes involve the appearance of "higher" or "modernized" sharks and rays: galeoids, squaloids, and batoids. Those of the Osteichthyes followed the appearance of the subholostean-holostean structural lines. The third peaks of the Osteichthyes follow the appearance of teleosts, now the dominant fishes.

In the probable but not absolutely established occurrence of two peaks of reptilian differentiation, one late Paleozoic and one early Mesozoic, the first involves the cotylosaurian-synapsid level (the two groups being adaptively and structurally very similar although their different fates have caused their radical separation in the usual classifications). The second set of peaks follows in regular sequence after appearance of the archosaurian level of organization in the Triassic.

A classic example of supposed "explosive" evolution and its correlation with diastrophism is the "explosion" of mammals supposed to initiate the Cenozoic and to be simultaneous with, if not caused by, the Laramide Revolution. But in fact the most basic event, the origin of placentals, occurred sometime well before the end of the Cretaceous. Most of the orders of early Cenozoic mammals did not appear at the Cretaceous-Paleocene boundary, but straggled in over a span of some 20 million years. The rate of appearance of new genera was low in the Paleocene and it did not reach its climax, its most truly "expolsive" phase, until the Pliocene, perhaps 60 million years after the end of the Cretaceous. When did the "explosion" occur? Certainly not at the Cretaceous-Paleocene boundary, and claimed relationship to the Laramide Revolution must surely be viewed with suspicion.

The most fundamental events of all within the span of vertebrate history, the origins of the classes, are not "explosions" in any sense, since each class is rare and little varied when it first appears, but these most major first appearances also follow a biologic sequence which seems to have no possible correlation with tectonic episodes dividing the periods and eras. Such appearances do not regularly occur at the beginning of periods. The Agnatha appear in the middle (or possibly late) Ordovician, Placodermi in late Silurian, Chondrichthyes and Osteichthyes in early Devonian, Amphibia in late Devonian, Reptilia in middle or late Pennsylvanian, Aves and Mammalia in middle Jurassic. (Mammals may have appeared in the late Triassic, as usually stated, but at present most of the supposed Triassic mammals appear to be reptiles by definition, and all may be.) Although some, at least, of these classes may have originated considerably before their first known appearances, it would be purely arbitrary to postulate origins at times of preceding diastrophic climaxes. Moreover no class of vertebrates and few of the major structural grades within the classes appear during or immediately after the two greatest tectonic episodes of the span of vertebrate history, the Appalachian Revolution and the Laramide Revolution.

## SUCCESSION AND REPLACEMENT

The climaxes or peaks of rate of appearance of new groups among the vertebrate classes form a fairly regular progression which clearly is not random. Or rather, they form two progressions, one for the primarily finned, aquatic types, the "fishes" (Classes Agnatha, Placodermi, Chondrichthyes, and Osteichthyes), and one for the primarily footed, amphibious to terrestrial types, the tetrapods (classes Amphibia, Reptilia, and Mammalia, with the Aves, not here discussed, forming a separate major ecological type of their own).

The succession involved here seems, again, to be evolutionary in a sense primarily biological, and I see no clear evidence for correlation of its main events with purely physical changes such as mountain-building. The most probable interpretation seems to be that at intervals some branch from an earlier radiation reaches a superior adaptive status which enables it largely (seldom com-

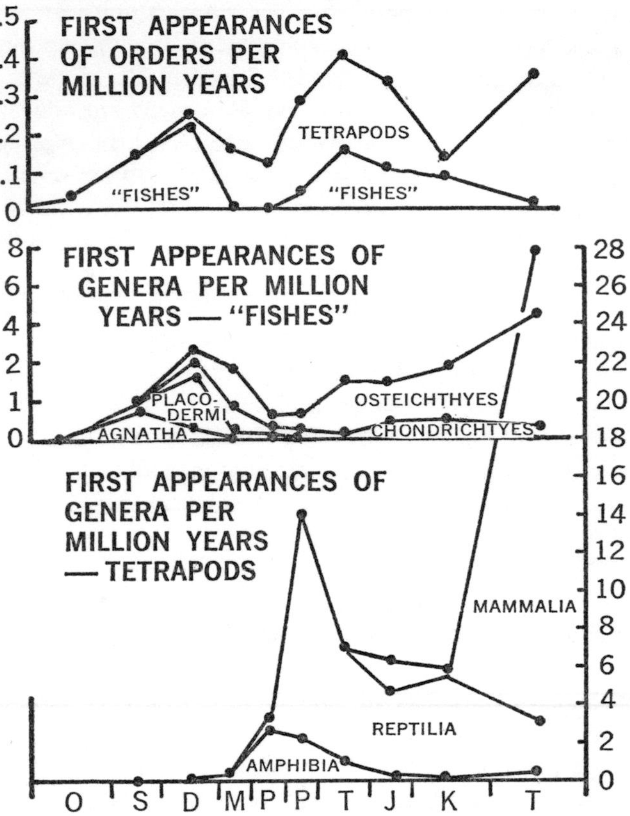


Fig. 4. Graphs of first appearances of orders per million years for vertebrates as a whole and of first appearances of genera per million years for "fishes" and for tetrapods. Time scale and general convention of construction as in Figs. 2, 3.

pletely) to replace earlier forms living over somewhat the same environmental range. In taxonomic terms, a new class, subclass, or superorder arises and the sequence of ordinal down to generic and specific "explosive" phases follows, as outlined above.

The sequence of such phases in the Agnatha, Placodermi, and

Chondrichthyes plus Osteichthyes is quite clear from Ordovician to about the end of the Paleozoic. (See Figs. 2, 4.) The ordinal climax of each group coincides approximately with the generic climax of the preceding group. In the Pennsylvanian and Permian, with no radically different or successional new adaptive type on the scene, the rates of appearances of new groups in Chondrichthyes and Osteichthyes fall to low points and evolution of "fishes" becomes relatively stagnant. In this part of their history, Devonian through Permian, Chondrichthyes and Osteichthyes are not successional to each other but simultaneous and closely parallel in the rise and fall of rates of appearances. The two, together, and not either separately or each in succession, seem to replace the earlier "fishes." There is, in fact, evidence that most Chondrichthyes were then marine and most Osteichthyes freshwater, so that they parceled out the aquatic domain between them.

In the Mesozoic and Cenozoic, as many Osteichthyes became marine, there is no longer simultaneity in "explosions" of these two classes, but a complex succession seesawing from Osteichthyes in the Triassic to Chondrichthyes in the Jurassic to Cretaceous and back to Osteichthyes in the Cretaceous to Recent.

Succession of "explosive" episodes among the tetrapods is simpler and rather obvious throughout. (See Figs. 3, 4.) The only complications in the Amphibian-Reptile-Mammal sequence are in relatively minor points and need not be discussed in this broader summary.

## EXTINCTIONS, SURVIVALS, AND TOTALS

Although this study is mainly devoted to episodes of appearance of new groups of vertebrates, some of the more striking related features of total expansion and contraction may be briefly mentioned.

Changes in total numbers of taxonomic units between any two times depend on a balance of four factors:

(*1*) Splitting up of single groups into two or more.

(*2*) Transformation of single groups to the point recognized as origin of new groups at the same taxonomic level.
(*3*) Survival of groups without change sufficient for recognition at the given taxonomic level.
(*4*) Disappearance of groups, without known descendants.

As the data are usually set up, these factors are not so clearly distinguishable and cannot be accurately analyzed. Such analysis can be made (although even here with some difficulty in categorization) for a few, small, exceptionally well-known and well-studied groups, such as the horses. For most groups and particularly for large groups such as those involved in the present summary, the data do not as yet exist, or are so incomplete that they would not repay the great labor of accurate analysis. In broader studies at present, therefore, the data used reflect the interplay of these factors, but do not adequately indicate the contribution of each. "First appearances" included contributions from both (*1*) and (*2*), without distinction, although (*1*) increases the total and (*2*) does not. In a continuous sequence, the number of first appearances due to

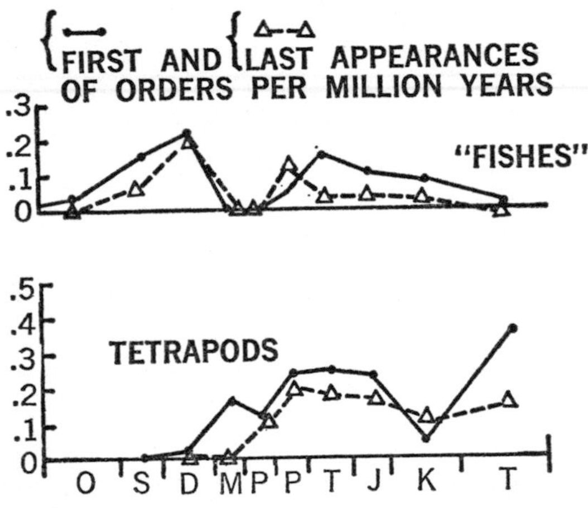


Fig. 5. Graphs of first and last appearances of orders per million years in "fishes" and in tetrapods. Time scale and general construction as in Figs. 2–4.

(*2*) increases with the length of the time unit used, although this misleading effect can be eliminated if first appearances are plotted relative to time, as in most of the graphs here presented.

"Last appearances" include contributions from both (*2*) and (*4*), again without distinction, although those due to (*4*) decrease the (subsequent) total and those due to (*2*) do not. Again, the last appearances due to transformation, (*2*), tend to be proportional to the time covered, and their real significance is not evident unless they are plotted relative to time. First and last appearances due to (*2*) are equal in number and balance each other exactly. The last appearances in any given time unit affect the total not in the same but in the following time unit.

Survivals from one time unit to the next, (*3*), tend to maintain the total level without change and are readily tabulated but are of obscure and variable significance. The number of survivals obviously decreases greatly as the length of the (essentially arbitrary) used time unit increases, and this confusing effect cannot be eliminated simply by plotting survivals relative to time. (In fact, this merely exaggerates the defect; plotting the reciprocal figure does give a more reliable result, but one still difficult to comprehend and interpret.) The tabulation or plotting of survivals has little or no clear significance unless the time unit used is considerably shorter than the average time span of the taxonomic unit used. Since the average span of vertebrate genera is less than that of a geological period, study of survival in genera is not useful on the scale of broad summary used in the present short contribution. Orders of vertebrates do tend to persist considerably longer than one geological period and so study of their survival from one period to another does have some usefulness (see Fig. 6 and text, below).

Figures for last appearances of genera or other small taxonomic units tend, unless the time scale used is more refined than is generally practicable for large groups, simply to run parallel to the figures for first appearances. This has two causes. First, the last appearances due to (2) in the list of factors given above are always equal in number to first appearances from the same cause and occur, theoretically, at the same point in time. Second, last

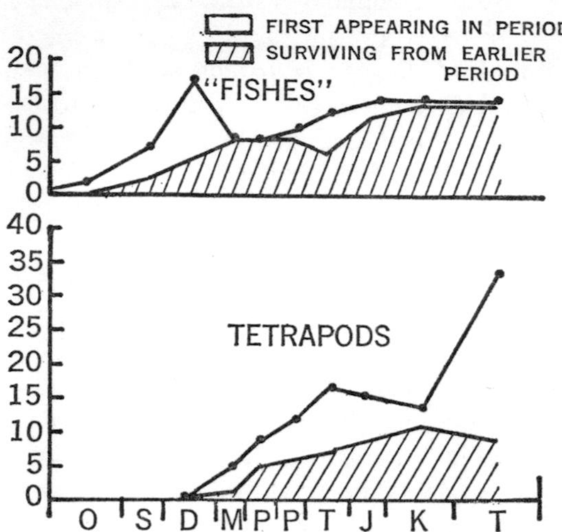


Fig. 6. Graphs of numbers of known orders of "fishes" and of tetrapods. The absolute total, not the number per million years, is indicated for each period. The height of the line above the cross-hatched area indicates the part contributed to the total by orders surviving from earlier periods. Time scale as in Figs. 2–5.

appearances representing true extinction, (*4*), tend to be proportional to total numbers and to be accelerated by increase in first appearances. There is normally a time lag in this case, but in the case of smaller taxonomic units it may be too short to be clear unless the data are quite exceptionally good and a brief time unit can be used.

Even at the level of orders, figures for first and for last appearances tend to run parallel (Fig. 5), although some significant interplay can be seen. For "fishes" the Devonian was a time of maximum rates both for first and for last appearances. This is a reflection of replacement. The peak of first appearances is due to rise of the

Chondrichthyes and Osteichthyes and the peak of last appearances is due to waning of the Agnatha and Placodermi. In the Mississippian and Pennsylvanian both first and last appearances of orders of "fishes" dropped to a minimum. (For genera, this minimum was Pennsylvanian to Permian. See Fig. 2.) During this time, the successful forms in the Devonian competition simply tended to survive with relatively little change. In the Permian, last appearances increased markedly without equal increase in first appearances; this is the only period in which last appearances were more numerous than first appearances of orders of "fishes." In combination with the drop of last appearances and rise of first appearances in the Triassic, this reflects a radical turnover of basic types of "fishes" from Permian to Triassic. After the Triassic there are no marked changes. Both first and last appearances of orders dropped steadily (and first appearances and totals of genera rose steadily) as the broad structural grades introduced in the Triassic survived and proliferated at lower taxonomic levels.

Among tetrapods (four-legged vertebrates), the equal first and last appearance rates of the Pennsylvanian and high for both in the Permian and Triassic accompany rapid turnover among early amphibians and reptiles and the beginning of replacement of some of the former by the latter. The drop in both rates in the Cretaceous, with last appearances becoming for the only time more frequent than first appearances, followed by a rise of first appearances far above last, repeats in geologically briefer time and with some differences the sort of episode seen among fishes in the late Paleozoic and early Mesozoic.

The total of known groups at any time is of course the sum of first appearances and survivors from the preceding time unit (Fig. 6). The number of survivors, in turn, is the total for the last period minus last appearances in that period. As regards orders, the course and balance of these various factors and their results are sufficiently shown in Figs. 5, 6.

In view of the picture as a whole, several periods of major evolutionary activity of different sorts stand out. The most striking of these seem to be:

DEVONIAN: Rapid turnover from earlier to later major groups of "fishes." High extinction rates for older types.

Extremely high basic origination rates for many sorts of "fishes," to be followed in subsequent periods by their diversification in lower taxonomic categories.

Origin of tetrapods.

PERMIAN TO TRIASSIC: Among both "fishes" and tetrapods, strongly pronounced turnover, with high last appearance rates in the Permian, at least, and high first appearance rates in the Triassic. (These major changes concern mainly the Osteichthyes and the Reptilia.)

CRETACEOUS TO TERTIARY: No definite climax or crisis among "fishes," but strongly marked tetrapod turnover involved in decline of the reptiles and rise of the mammals.

It has long been realized that these were major episodes in vertebrate history and the present conclusion only confirms and to some extent quantifies what was already well-known. It should, however, be emphasized that these episodes are of long continuation and that they are not sharply defined in time, even as to their beginnings. It has, for instance, already been stressed that the essential features of the Cretaceous-Tertiary crisis cannot really be localized just at the boundary between those periods. The episodes are parts of a long and essentially continuous process.

The Permian-Triassic and Cretaceous-Tertiary major evolutionary changes do coincide with era boundaries, or, rather, the accepted era boundaries occur within the long and vaguely defined span embracing these evolutionary events. The era boundaries, in turn, coincide with mooted major tectonic episodes, the reality or true nature and extent of which are for others to judge. There may be some degree of causal connection within the complex totality of evolutionary processes involved and it is unlikely that physical events played no part in these evolutionary episodes. The conclusion that theirs was the decisive and necessary part is not supported by the biological evidence and may be gratuitous. It is also to be remembered that the era boundaries were established in large part on paleontological grounds, so that their coincidence with evolutionary events is not really, in another sense of the word, a coincidence.

## CONCLUSIONS

In certain particular cases, strong or even startling evolutionary effects can be clearly traced to physical, geographic and tectonic causes. Completion of the Central American land bridge in the Pliocene was followed by geologically sudden and radical changes in the fauna of South America. Rates of extinction rose rapidly among native South American groups of mammals particularly, and rates of diversification or proliferation became extremely rapid among groups introduced from North America. Similar results followed rise of the Bering bridge between the Old World and the New in the late Eocene after long isolation through the middle parts of the period. In such cases the correlation of biological and physical events is obviously real. It is clear that such events have repeatedly occurred and constitute a large and important part of the history of life. They do not, however, as far as can be seen, account for the origins of important new types or structural grades of animals. The episodes of proliferation that follow them are also of secondary importance in the whole picture of earth history. Even when continent-wide, they are local with respect to the earth as a whole, and the proliferation is on low taxonomic levels, dispersion into new living spaces generally by replacement of older, ecologically similar, and often more or less closely related previous residents.

The physical concomitants of such episodes are also and still more strictly local. Relatively slight local warping of the crust in a small area of Central America or of the Bering region, for instance, is all that need occur. No widespread or major diastrophic crisis is required or is evidenced. On the other hand, world-wide and revolutionary orogeny and diastrophism could occur without having any particular results of this sort, because it need not affect the small areas that happen to be crucial. It is significant that the two examples given above (and many others that could be added) did not occur at times of disturbances or revolutions usually recognized by adherents of the theory of periodic world-wide diastrophism and did not occur at or shortly after conventional epoch or period boundaries.

It is probable that such events are sometimes involved in episodes that are important details in the broader picture of biological history. This may be true, for instance, of the changes used in fixing the Cretaceous-Tertiary boundary, especially disappearance of the last dinosaurs and appearance of a meager vanguard of Cenozoic mammalian types in the (few and local) collecting regions where these facts can be ascertained. The geographic event may then have determined a useful time datum and may enable us to draw a boundary in a given region. Still that is not evidence that the geographic event itself was more than a local crustal warp at some place or other, or that it did more than set the precise time of evolutionary events that would in any case have occurred at about that time in the sweep of the long, continuous evolutionary process.

The evidence summarized in this essay is consistent with the view that most of the broad features of vertebrate history might have been much the same if the earth's crust had been static (providing that the surface remained sufficiently varied and with large connected and nearly connected land and sea areas). Crustal movements may have had essential roles only as regards details of timing and of distribution, important details in some cases but still only details. The older and still perhaps more common belief in causal synchronism of periodic world-wide evolutionary and diastrophic episodes is certainly not disproven, but the evidence runs rather more against than for it. The most likely points at which physical events may have had decisive influence are the extinctions of aquatic vertebrates around the end of the Permian and of terrestrial vertebrates around the end of the Cretaceous.

There is a well-marked periodicity in vertebrate history, especially as regards successive peaks and valleys of high and low proliferation of new groups, in one class after another or sometimes within one class at different times. Taken as a whole, these peaks are rather evenly distributed in geologic time and have no clear segregation that could correspond with periodic crustal crises. Within any one major group, the peaks at different levels of adaptive differentiation spread very widely in geologic time, over spans up to 100 million years or more, which makes difficult or impossible their connection with particular tectonic events more sharply defined, as at period boundaries. The regularity of this long process is, moreover, suggestive of continuity of evolutionary forces acting regardless of periodic physical events despite the periodicity of some of the results. The "explosions" in evolution are not really isolated occurrences or brief even in the sense of a few million years of geologic time. They seem, rather, to be merely regular, shorter episodes or manifestations in a more basic process which is really secular and not periodic.

The origins of classes, orders, or other taxonomic units, either singly or in the accelerated clusters of "explosions," do not, in the record, show any apparently causal correlation with epoch or period boundaries, beyond the extent to which these boundaries have themselves been set to correspond with some convenient evolutionary marker. The important Paleozoic-Mesozoic boundary, for instance, occurs within and near the climax of a radical faunal change, which is used to define that boundary, but it does not coincide with, or even approximate, the time of origin of any basic new type of vertebrate or any peak in proliferation of some group. It is marked mainly by negative, not positive, evolution, by extinction. The subsequent positive faunal changes may have been stimulated by preceding extinctions but may also have been the outcome of events that occurred much earlier or indeed of a whole chain of events back to the origin of the vertebrates or of life.

As far as this evidence goes, then, diastrophism and other physical events continue to hold a place in the totality of factors that are, inseparably, the cause of evolution. They cannot be promoted to a role as leading and distinct cause of the major features of vertebrate evolution. The related but different and more particular theory of accelerated evolution during rhythmic or periodic diastrophic disturbances or revolutions deserves, at best, a verdict of "not proven." For the vertebrates, at least, it may be proper to add "improbable."

## REFERENCE

Romer, A. S., 1945, *Vertebrate Paleontology:* 2nd ed., ix, 687 pp., illus., University of Chicago Press, Chicago, Ill.

• • •

# PART 3

*The third essay in the collection consists, in large part, of an analysis of vertebrate paleontology itself. The discipline and its practices are examined, its history as a science is reviewed and certain conclusions are drawn, the latter chiefly concerning its scientific, educational, and economic value. Finally, some thought is also given to philosophical and even religious aspects of current theory in this area of natural science.*

# Some Problems of Vertebrate Paleontology

Paleontologists sometimes argue among themselves over whether they really are, or should be, geologists or biologists. The discussion is usually futile and sometimes absurd. Paleontology is characterized, but is not fully defined, by having its own objective subject matter: fossils. Fossils occur in rocks, and they are organisms. Their extended study necessarily overlaps widely into both of the broader (or more miscellaneous) sciences of geology and biology. Without really departing from his own science, a paleontologist may even find himself engaged in work that does not directly involve any fossils and that is quite strictly geological (for example, sedimentation) or biological (for example, genetics).

Traditionally, invertebrate paleontologists have been more geologically, and vertebrate paleontologists more biologically, oriented. The tradition arose because invertebrate paleontology, both commercial and academic, has always had an important role as a service branch of geology, supplying most of the correlations needed for stratigraphy and for historical geology in general. Vertebrate paleontology has had few commercial applications, and it has tended to attract students who were interested in studying organisms as such more than in rendering a practical service to geologists. That tradition still has an evident influence on the two fields, but the distinction is now breaking down. Both invertebrate and vertebrate paleontology are becoming broader, and paleontologists in both fields are becoming more diverse in approaches, methods, and aims.

In view of the great and still increasing spread of subject matter, a major problem of vertebrate paleontology is that of manpower. There simply are not enough vertebrate paleontologists, or enough positions for them, for adequate and consistent cultivation of the whole subject. Definition is difficult and may even be invidious, but if by "vertebrate paleontologist" we mean someone who has vertebrate paleontology as his primary field and who is working continuously in it at an independent, professional research level, in 1960 there were about 65 vertebrate paleontologists in North America and perhaps as many more in all the rest of the world.[1] They are, however, backed up by a corps of technical personnel who do little independent research themselves but who greatly promote such research. It is further true that a significant proportion of the important research in vertebrate paleontology is done by people who are not primarily professionals in this subject but who work in it occasionally or marginally. The total number of people now making some contribution to the science runs well into the hundreds. Nevertheless, it is an unfortunate fact that some brilliant new possibilities opening up in the field of vertebrate paleontology are not being followed up simply because there are not enough specialists to work on all of them.

The basic essentials for continued progress in vertebrate paleontology are still the same as the earliest activities, and will continue to be so as far as can be seen into the future. Involved here are the flow of new discoveries and data from the field, laboratory preparation of specimens, and study of their morphology and taxonomy. Much the greatest part of current effort is devoted to these classical but continuously necessary activities. There are still new fossil fields to be discovered. Renewed collecting in known fields, often by campaigns over many years, is necessary to make more nearly adequate collections and to provide field data up to modern standards, which are far more rigorous than the standards of even a few years ago. Laboratory preparation is still a bottleneck, one of the reasons why vertebrate paleontology is often a slow science. Decades may necessarily elapse between beginning a large project with field work and ending it with final publication of the results. In addition, almost all the basic taxonomy of a generation or more ago now requires revision in the light not only of new materials but also of new principles and standards. (This does not mean that the earlier work was wasted; the new principles and standards arose from it, and many of its data are as useful as ever.)

It is precisely here, in its most basic activities, that vertebrate paleontology has many of its most striking recent discoveries, and improvements in techniques and approaches, and also has its continuing problems. It must be stressed again that here is not only the great bulk of work in vertebrate paleontology but also the most fundamental aspect of that work. It is further to be emphasized that much of the current progress and many of the most pressing problems are on the geological side of the subject, in sedimentation, stratigraphy, correlation, chronology, and related topics. Nevertheless, and solely because of limitations of space, those parts of the subject are treated only incidentally in the following discussion. My purpose here is to consider problems of broader and more theoretical biological interpretation that arise after the basic data, taxonomic and geologic, are in hand. Even within that more limited scope, the treatment can be only a sampling and an exemplification of a few problems and in no sense a review of the field.[2] Some aspects of morphology and systematics, closely related to the basic data, are considered briefly before certain interpretive problems more removed from that level are treated.

## MORPHOLOGY

Even in its 18th-century beginnings, vertebrate paleontology was never confined to collection, preparation, description, and classification. It is, however, especially characteristic of the work done in recent years—the 1940's into 1960's—that there has been a great irruption of new ideas, new goals of interpretation, renewed efforts toward theorizing in broader ways and at more generalized levels. At present there seems to be some reaction against that tendency, and a certain ambivalence has arisen in the profession. This is not a clear-cut dichotomy into an *école des faits* and an *école des idées* but only a difference in the points of view of those who would lay greater stress on one or the other of what are, after all, mutually dependent and equally necessary aspects of the same whole. There is the need, on one hand, for more detailed, complete, and accurate anatomical observation, description, and illustration,[3] but also, on the other, for generalization and theoretical formulation that alone can make such data meaningful.

On the observational side, vertebrate comparative anatomy, not only of fossil but also of recent animals, has become largely the province of vertebrate paleontology. It is indicative that outstanding textbooks in that field are those by Romer, a vertebrate paleontologist. All vertebrate paleontologists have perforce been anatomists, but a modern school of morphology has arisen largely through the efforts of Watson in England, Gregory in the United States, and Stensiö in Sweden and has been carried on especially by their respective students. To take a single school as an example, Stensiö and his students have investigated the anatomy of many early vertebrates in almost incredible detail and have produced reconstructions that often incidentally have striking esthetic values.[4] The methods involve not only delicate macroscopic preparation but also thin sections, serial sections, and plastic reconstructions. Study of all fossil species in equal detail is neither desirable nor possible, but application of this approach to at least some characteristic members of all major groups is an eventual necessity, and a beginning has barely been made. As regards later vertebrates, Whitmore's study of some Oligocene artiodactyl skulls is not quite, but unfortunately almost, unique.[5]

The most ardent advocates of descriptive anatomy for its own sake do not deny the need for some generalizing principles. In this respect there are two schools. A small group consisting mainly of Naef, Kälin, and their students, notably Zangerl in the United States, has approached comparative anatomy as a self-contained subject with its own principles independent of those of any other biological discipline.[6] For them, generalization is by abstraction of a "Morphotypus," which is essentially the archetype of the pre-evolutionary typological idealistic morphologists or *Naturphilosophen* exemplified by Goethe. For the great majority of vertebrate paleontological morphologists, however, the central principle is now that of evolutionary homology—derivation of structures from a common ancestry and their modification in the course of phylogenetic descent.

From the latter point of view, greatest interest attaches to major transformations that are involved also in important problems of systematics and of evolutionary theory. The fish-amphibian transformation is being studied especially by Jarvik, in the laboratories under Stensiö's direction,[4] and also by Westoll, Romer, and others. As another example, the reptile-mammal transition, outlined in a general way long since, is now under new attack in greater phylogenetic and morphogenetic detail by, among many others, Brink and Crompton in South Africa; Watson, Parrington, and Westoll in England; and Romer, Patterson, and Olson in the United States.[7] This transition was a main subject of a colloquium in Oxford, England, in 1960. Another classical problem now under renewed attack concerns the evolutionary morphogenesis of mammalian molar teeth. One of the triumphs of paleontological morphology of the late 19th and early 20th centuries was the discovery by Cope and Osborn that therian (that is, both marsupial and placental) molar dentitions all went through a common stage now called tribosphenic. The origin of the tribosphenic dentition, however, is still quite uncertain, but it is being studied with new evidence from Mesozoic mammals and mammal-like reptiles. That was a main subject of another international meeting in 1960, organized by Vandebroek in Brussels.[8]

Classic approaches to morphology, even when evolutionary in principle, deal typically with individual structures in a somewhat static way. Newer, more dynamic approaches are now also being followed. One of these approaches, already with a rather large literature and applications of well-developed methodology to a great variety of vertebrate groups, deals with ontogenetic structural changes, especially as influenced by relative growth.[9] Another, which seems at least equally promising but still presents serious unsolved methodological problems, has to do with covariation, correlation, and association of anatomical character complexes within populations and among groups of related forms.[10] Studies of the more classic sort are still of prime importance and not to be disparaged, but the most striking progress in morphological principles will probably be in these newer fields in the near future, and in work relating morphology to the biology of the individual.[11]

## SYSTEMATICS

As early as the 18th century fossil vertebrates were being classified according to the same system as Recent animals, and of course this still is, and always must be, a basic and principal activity in this science, perhaps the most basic of all. Since Linnaeus and Cuvier, in addition to innumerable more superficial changes of form and content, there have been two deep revolutions in the principles of systematics. Vertebrate paleontology has been influenced by and has contributed to both. First was the change from special creation to evolution as an explanation for the diversity of life, and hence to the order in nature which makes classification possible. Second, more subtle and harder to grasp but equally fundamental, was the change from classification in which categories were defined by typological abstractions of constant characters and individuals were the members of taxa * to classification with phylogenetically defined categories and with varying populations as the members of taxa. In the latter revolution, not yet complete, vertebrate paleontologists have been both leaders and laggards. Some

* A taxon (plural, taxa) is a group of organisms formally recognized and named in a technical classification.

were pioneers in using the conceptually statistical, sample-population approach to taxa and in using phylogenetic categories, and others still do not adopt either of those concepts.[12]

The problems of obtaining adequate, unbiased samples and, alternatively, of making proper allowances and corrections for inadequacies and biases are particularly acute in paleontological systematics. Almost all vertebrate paleontologists have become aware of those special problems, most of which have been identified and listed, but there are still few specific and concrete studies. Two examples of the kind of studies that are pertinent here may be cited. Olson has presented a model theoretical and practical study of size distributions in samples of growing animals.[13] Shotwell has attempted to separate members of proximal and distant communities in quarry accumulations by calculating the number of bones recovered per individual.[14] It is irrelevant, for our purposes, that Shotwell's method may prove to have restricted applicability.[15] Ideas of that sort and their testing, both by theoretical models and by particular actual occurrences, are badly needed if we are to make adequate evaluations of the fossil record and place generalizations about it on a sounder basis.

Changes in the concept of species and in the interpretation of samples in recent years have been so profound that practically no "species" of fossil vertebrates described more than 20 years ago, and not all of those described since then, can now be taken at face value as properly defined and biologically significant species of natural populations. Fortunately, that situation is changing now, and biologically sound specific descriptions are so numerous in recent work as hardly to need exemplification. One consequence of the previous situation has been that most sound paleontological studies of systematics, and of the evolutionary processes that underlie systematics, have hitherto necessarily been above the species level. Knowledge of structure and processes within species, or between closely related species, has come mostly from recent animals and has lacked a significant time dimension. It is, however, now clear that such studies can be based on some fossil groups with particularly favorable sampling conditions, and this indicates a whole field of important problems to which vertebrate paleontology may soon be expected to make more significant contributions.

As regards the systematics of higher categories, the situation in vertebrate paleontology has long been more favorable. Most of our theoretical understanding of the nature of such categories and of how the corresponding taxa have evolved has been provided by vertebrate paleontology, and this is one of its most active current fields of research. Moreover, in most groups of vertebrates (teleost fishes and birds are the outstanding exceptions) actual classification at high-categorical levels is now based primarily on paleontological data. Many of the important current problems in this field arise from increasing evidence of some degree of polyphyly and parallel evolution at high levels—evidence which makes the delimitation of, for instance, the classes Amphibia, Reptilia, and especially Mammalia increasingly difficult and disputed.[16] (See Fig. 7.) Among the many examples of similar problems in systematics at successively lower levels,[17] mention may be made of work on the separation of the orders Insectivora and Primates (or the dismemberment of those orders); on recognition of suborders of the order Rodentia, which probably does not have natural suborders,[18] and on redefinition of genera and phyletic lines in the supposedly well-known horse family.[19] The examples are all among mammals, but others of the kind occur in every vertebrate class.

## FUNCTIONAL BIOLOGY OF INDIVIDUALS AND OF SPECIES

Vertebrate paleontologists have always attempted to draw inferences about general functional characteristics of prehistoric animals —how they moved, what they ate, and the like. Such inferences were based almost entirely (and necessarily, as it seemed) on analogies with similar, living animals. They tended to become mere fantasies when referring to structures for which there are no such analogies—for example, the dorsal fins of some Permian pelycosaurs, the "hoods" of some duckbilled dinosaurs, or the claws of

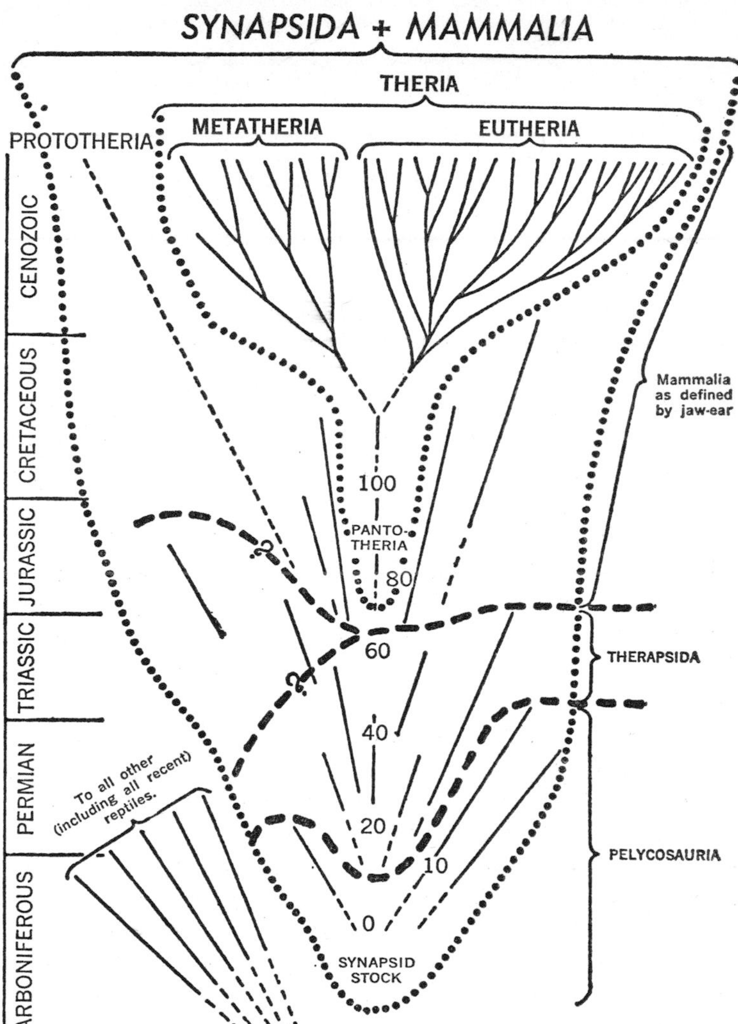


Fig. 7. A problem in phylogeny and systematics: relationships of the Mammalia to their ancestry are shown schematically. The light lines represent the general pattern (but not the detail) or phylogeny as now known. Heavy dashed lines separate successive taxa as now usually recognized. Numerals are estimates of degree of advance (in per cent) from fully reptilian to fully mammalian basic characteristics.

the phylogenetically ungulate chalicotheres. Such analogical, and often more subjective and anecdotal than scientifically inductive, studies reached their height in the *"Palaeobiologie"* of Abel, half a century ago. After Abel, analogies, quite properly, were still sought, but for some years the field seemed to have little further potential for the production of new ideas or of more rigorous methods.

Here we are in the midst of a definite revival. Problems are being more broadly conceived but more strictly defined, and better methods are being devised to solve them. In part, the current approach involves greater precision and better analogical evidence in application to the same kinds of problems as those attacked earlier in a looser way. This is the approach in reconstructions and functional analysis of musculature (for example, of ceratopsians, by Haas,[20] following earlier work by Lull and others) or in interpretation of limb function from trackways (for example, in amphibians, by Peabody,[21] also following and improving on earlier work by many hands). In other instances, earlier intuitive judgments have been replaced by quantitative experimental data derived from working models—for example, in studies of early reptilian auditory function, by Hotton.[22]

Similar use of models has already been made in studies of a variety of functional problems (for example, of locomotion in early fishes and in pterodactyls), and the method is capable of much further extension. It has the advantage not only of giving quantitative results but also of being applicable to structures without close analogs in living animals. In some instances study by means of mathematical, rather than physical, models and analyses has the same advantages. For example, the problem of the pelycosaur dorsal fin, mentioned above, seems essentially solved by Romer's demonstration that the regression relationship of fin area to body volume is appropriate to the functioning of the fin as a temperature-regulating mechanism.[23] (See Fig. 8.)

Those successful attacks on old problems by new methods are supplemented in an even more interesting way by the formulation and at least partial solution of quite new problems, either overlooked previously or believed insoluble on the basis of fossil materials. An important example is the biological consideration not only of single structures but of whole organ systems as developmental and correlational fields. Butler pioneered in that approach some time since,[24] and it is being carried further not only by Butler but also by others, notably Kurtén [25] (See Fig. 9.) Kurtén, who is particularly ingenious in quantitative biological approaches to paleontology, has also developed life tables, survivorship curves, and age pyramids for fossil populations.[25]

Such studies of structures and of populations broaden the interpretive capacity of paleontology by bringing in functional and dynamic aspects previously amenable to profitable study only among living animals. They have, however, still greater potential importance because they can bring an extended time dimension to such studies and thus supply an evolutionary basis not attainable from study of recent animals alone. That potential is barely beginning to be realized in the present pioneering phase, but the possibilities are certainly great.

## FAUNAS, ECOLOGY, AND BIOGEOGRAPHY

A next step in deepening and broadening the contributions of vertebrate paleontology to general biology is the consideration not only of individuals and of specific populations but also of whole faunas. This, again, is not a new field but goes back in a tentative and subjective way to the very beginnings of the science. In retrospect, it is seen to have had a turning point and to have begun to enter a new era with the work of W. D. Matthew in the first three decades of this century. Since then, and at a pace that is still accelerating, problems outlined or exemplified by Matthew have been attacked by more varied, more rigorous, and in good part more quantitative methods, and new kinds of problems in the same general field have been formulated.

Here the ideal is the functional study of whole biotas, plants, invertebrates, and vertebrates in relation to their environments, to earlier and later biotas, and to the contemporaneous biotas of other

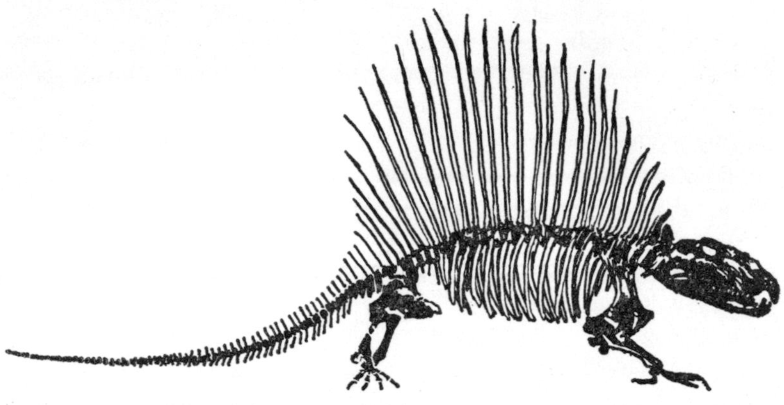

Fig. 8. A paleobiological problem: the Permian reptile *Dimetrodon,* with a large dorsal fin of long-disputed function, now interpreted as a heat-regulating device. (Museum of Comparative Zoology, Harvard University)

areas. Needless to say, this ideal has not been and in fact cannot be fully achieved; not even a recent biota has been fully described, still less functionally interpreted, in accordance with the ideal. Nevertheless, it is being approached in numerous and varied, necessarily more restricted and somewhat piecemeal, studies. Data for this kind of study come from all the fields that have been previously mentioned, and from still others. Here the geological basis, which I do not have space to consider, becomes particularly important—especially sedimentation, geochronology, correlation, and stratigraphy, including microstratigraphy, in which faunal associations are tied in very precisely, down to millimeters in some instances, with successive stratigraphic levels. Sampling problems, already briefly mentioned, are here acute, and there is great need for better understanding of the factors that act between the living fauna and the preservation of part of it in fossil state, as well as factors involved in the formation of fossil deposits in general. Study of such factors has been called "biostratonomy" by Weigelt and "taphonomy" by Efremov, although it may be a little premature to designate as distinct sciences fields in which, unfortunately, there is as yet little concrete accomplishment.

Basic biological data on this subject are the taxa present in a given fossil association and their relative abundance. The present tendency and need is to narrow specifications to the point where a fossil association may, perhaps with minor exceptions, be taken as representative of a single ecological community. M. C. McKenna, among others, has recently exemplified the graphic and tabular presentation of such data, his examples being strictly localized mammalian faunules within a broader regional fauna of early Eocene age.[26] A next step involves inference about the ecological characteristics of the various taxa and thence about the ecological structure of the community. The community characteristics are related in turn to the environmental situation, and in favorable instances community differences can be related to ecological environmental distributions on a local or microgeographic basis. A brilliant example at this level has been provided by Olson, who in a sequence of Permian vertebrate faunas not only has demonstrated the microgeographic distribution of ecological types correlated with sedimentary facies (Fig. 10) but also has followed ecological and evolutionary changes through a sequence of environments over considerable periods of time.[27]

Biogeographical study at the next higher level, in which more strictly historical-evolutionary elements are in interplay with ecological factors, concerns the distributions of evolving species and faunas over larger areas, up to continental size. Of special interest here is the evolutionary origin and geographic emplacement of recent biotas within the various biotic regions of the world. There have been many studies at this level for particular groups of plants and animals, but mostly on the basis of living organisms only. Without some control by directly historical—that is, paleontological—evidence, such conclusions must be viewed with strong reservations. For mammals, especially, and particularly for those of Europe and North America, there is already an enormous accumulation of late Cenozoic specimens and data, but almost all of them have still to be analyzed adequately from this point of view.

There is here a particularly large number of fascinating problems soluble by materials at hand or readily obtainable and only awaiting students with the ability, interest, and time to work on them.

There are, to be sure, many published papers on geographic shifts of particular species and genera, and a few concerned with more extensive faunal associations, especially during late Cenozoic climate changes. An example is the recent demonstration by Hibbard of the southern movement of some warm-climate vertebrates in the United States as climates became cooler in the late Cenozoic.[28] For the most part, however, the scattered studies so far made lack both generality and precision. An example of a broader approach is Shotwell's study of morphological change, geographic

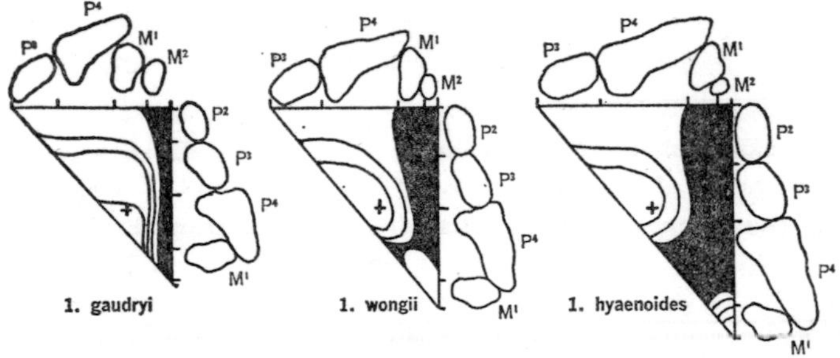


Fig. 9. Correlation fields in the dentitions of fossil mammals: upper-cheek teeth of three species of the Pliocene hyena *Ictitherium*. The triangular fields indicate the correlation between teeth diagrammatically indicated vertically above and horizontally to the right. For the black areas the coefficient of correlation $z$ is less than .50. The contours represent higher values, in steps of .10. (After B. Kurtén)

distribution, and correlation with distributional changes in vegetation for two related families of rodents from late Eocene to Recent in the western United States.[29] Here, as usual, the available data still are not wholly adequate, but this may be viewed as a sort of pilot study that indicates a profitable direction for future research.

Study on a still broader scale is that of the historical development of whole regional and continental faunas and of relationships among them. Darwin was already impressed by this subject as a young man when he collected fossil mammals in South America on the voyage of the *Beagle,* and in fact it was one of the two principal lines of evidence that converted him to belief in evolution. (The other was the differentiation and the evident affinities of birds in the Galápagos Islands.) Matthew devoted more detailed attention to the subject, and he has successors who have followed in his footsteps and have, with constantly improved data, gone well beyond him. The main outlines of Cenozoic and mostly mammalian faunal evolution are now well established for Europe, North America, and South America, and Eurasian–North American and North American–South American faunal relationships and interchanges are also fairly well understood.[30] Of course, even for these best-known sequences, innumerable details remain to be filled in, and the degree of precision is seriously limited by the still unsatisfactory status of intercontinental correlation. Elsewhere, great blocks of evidence are still lacking or are extremely inadequate—for example, for the whole Tertiary in Australia, the early Tertiary in Africa, and the early Paleocene throughout the world except for the Rocky Mountain region of the United States.

Currently accepted general principles of historical biogeography and its (rather few) special methods, such as the quantification of faunal resemblances,[31] are derived largely from paleomammalogy in the tradition of Darwin and Matthew. This is evident, for instance, in a fine recent treatise on the historical biogeography of nonmarine vertebrates, which happens to have been written not by a vertebrate paleontologist or a mammalogist but by an entomologist, Darlington.[32] Such studies, departing from a geological basis at one end, also have repercussions in geology at the other end. For example, mammalian migrations and faunal relationships practically rule out any real possibility that significant continental drift has occurred during the Cenozoic.

## EVOLUTION

It is an extraordinary but explicable fact that evolution was not discovered by vertebrate paleontologists; the rather complex explanation hinges on the inadequacy of data before 1859 and on the philosophy and prestige of Cuvier, the first professional vertebrate paleontologist. After publication of *The Origin of Species,* vertebrate paleontologists rapidly became evolutionists, and in the late 19th and early 20th centuries they developed three principal roles in this respect. First, they supplied clinching evidence of the truth of evolution. Second, along with the invertebrate paleontologists and the paleobotanists, they undertook to trace the actual history of evolving organisms. Third, they proposed various theories and so-called laws of evolution.

The truth of evolution has been adequately established long since, and although every paleontological discovery adds to the proof, the paleontologist's role in that connection is no longer important. Tracing the history of organisms is still a central purpose of paleontologists, who are now advancing more rapidly than ever but are still not even in full sight of this goal. The many problems and gaps in that field are not under consideration in this brief review. The third role is now more important than ever before, but its nature has changed radically in the last 20 years.[33]

An eminent vertebrate paleontologist, Lehman, recently declared: "One hardly believes in laws of evolution any longer." [33] He was not, of course, raising doubts about the fact of evolution but expressing disillusionment with some of the theoretical preoccupations of his predecessors and recommending stricter concentration on morphology. Early evolutionary vertebrate paleontologists were much concerned with developing generalizations, which they often incorrectly called "laws," on the basis of what they knew of the fossil record. Some of these generalizations have proved to be incorrect; others have had to be more or less profoundly modified; and a few have been validated as generalizations open to exception. Orthogenesis, which was not really first proposed by vertebrate paleontologists but was accepted by many of them and is still often considered a paleontological "law," is in the first category. As defined in the most usual of its many and sometimes conflicting definitions, it flatly is not true; lineages are not impelled by some internal or supernal force to keep on evolving indefinitely in the same direction.[33] "Dollo's law" of the irreversibility of evolution is an example of the second category. It was partly wrong as Dollo himself stated it, but it reflected a correct generalization now embraced in the broader statement of evolutionary irrevocability: organisms do not, as a rule, wholly return to any ancestral condition nor yet wholly lose effects of any ancestral condition.[33] Examples in the third category are "Cope's law," that individuals in evolving lineages tend to become larger as time goes on,[34] or "Williston's law,"[35] that repeated similar structures in individual organisms tend in the course of evolution to become less numerous and functionally more differentiated.[36] Both are frequently general tendencies, though there are numerous exceptions.

Such generalizations are still part of the interpretive instrumentation of vertebrate paleontologists, and it is not quite true that they no longer believe in what used to be called "laws of evolution." It is, however, true that this approach has proved rather sterile, has produced no really novel and striking ideas in the last generation or so, and probably deserves its present unpopularity. The whole effort to find laws in this field analogous to the laws of the physical sciences was methodologically mistaken.

Most of the early contributions of vertebrate paleontologists to theories of evolutionary factors and forces (as opposed to the descriptive generalizations that were mistaken for laws) also now seem sterile in retrospect. Cope developed his own form of Neo-Lamarckism, popular for a time but now wholly discredited. Osborn espoused a somewhat nebulous, idiosyncratic, vitalistic-finalistic theory never accepted by any of his colleagues. After making a good start in it, Scott abandoned the whole field of evolutionary theory as futile. Broom called in familiar spirits to explain evolution. Matthew took a somewhat naive form of Neo-Darwinism for granted and did little to test or to advance the theory. In each of these and in many other cases that could be cited, a significant

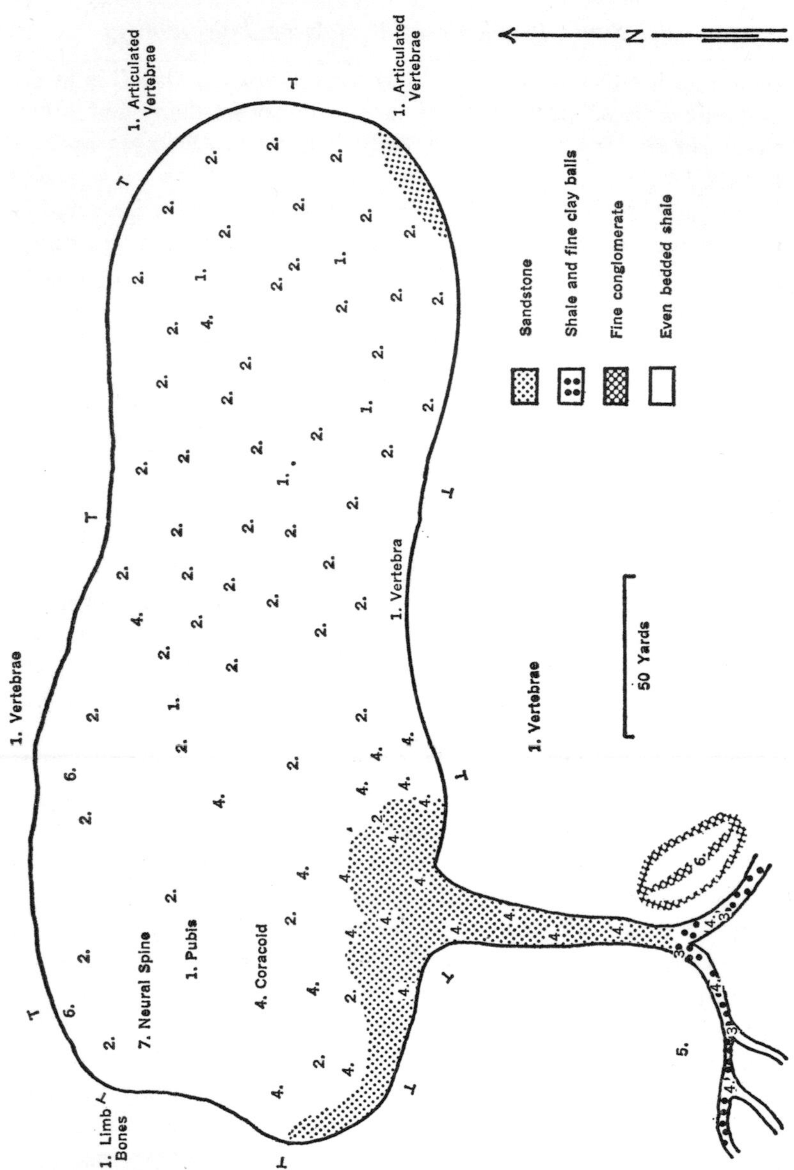


Fig. 10. An example of paleoecological data and interpretation. The map represents a Permian pond, its shore, and a small tributary stream, now represented by sediments, as keyed at lower right. The numbers indicate precise sites of discovery of different kinds of fossil vertebrates. Correlation of kinds of fossils with the ecological situation is evident. (After E. C. Olson)

factor is that the vertebrate paleontologists were operating in an almost watertight compartment. They tended to neglect and were sometimes quite ignorant of the progress of theoretical biology in other fields.

The situation now is very different. The main (not the only) body of evolutionary theory today, sometimes called "Neo-Darwinian" but usually and more appropriately "synthetic," arose largely as a synthesis between genetics and systematics, but it immediately expanded to embrace other and eventually all fields of the life sciences. Vertebrate paleontology early began to play a large and in some respects crucial role in that development, a role in which it is not compartmented but is firmly integrated with almost all the branches of biology. (Other paleontologists have of course also contributed importantly, but up to now more has been done by vertebrate paleontologists than by the others, probably because they tend to be more biologically oriented and because for certain groups they have particularly good bodies of pertinent and well analyzed data.)

In terms of the broadest aspect of its role, paleontology shows what has happened in the course of evolution over large groups of organisms and through long periods of time. In other words, paleontology specifies what really has to be explained by any explanatory theory of evolution. Put in its weakest and most negative form, the conclusion now most generally supported is that there is nothing in the fossil record that cannot conceivably be explained by the synthetic theory, or at least by an expanded and probably somewhat modified form of the theory. A note of caution and even in some respects of opposition has been sounded by some students, notably by Olson among vertebrate paleontologists.[37] In broadest essence, the criticisms point out that other explanations are *possible* and that the synthetic theory has not clearly explained *everything*—propositions that must certainly be granted by all reasonable students of the subject. The position of those of us who do open-mindedly support the synthetic theory is simply that no other explanations yet advanced seem to us nearly as probable, and that so far no phenomenon clearly established as real is plainly inexplicable under the synthetic theory or definitely contradicts it.

Within the general field of synthetic theory, paleontology provides concrete evidence and examples that can be obtained in no other way, covering periods of time not observable by experimentation or by neosystematics. Olson and other critics are certainly right and are playing a useful part in pointing out that *all* the phenomena revealed by paleontology do have to be explained, that these could conceivably controvert parts, at least, of the synthetic theory (although they have not done so), and that they must inevitably both expand and modify evolutionary theory.

One basic aspect of these problems is the firmer integration of paleontological and neontological studies and improvement of genetical interpretation of the fossil record. That involves especially studies of variation and heredity of characters that can be observed in fossils and for which control studies can be made on recent animals. Along with an increasing number of other students, Bader has recently devoted attention to this subject.[38] Work on morphological integration and structural correlation, previously mentioned, is also pertinent here. In a related field, Kurtén has been able to measure the intensity of mortality selection in some fossil populations and has found, as have a number of neontologists in parallel studies, that the intensity of natural selection on apparently trivial characters may be amazingly great.[39]

More peculiarly paleontological is the study of long-term and, as it turns out, usually changing trends in evolution. The literature of that subject is already very extensive and hardly needs exemplification, but fully adequate review and synthesis are still lacking.[33] A major necessity here is to establish unequivocally that an assembled morphological sequence does truly follow a temporal evolutionary sequence. Former belief in orthogenesis was largely bolstered by ignoring data on time sequence, and the same criticism may justly be leveled at some current work by vertebrate paleontologists of the "pure" morphological school.

The study of evolutionary rates is another complex subject that, in the nature of things, is almost entirely in the province of paleontology. Bader and Kurtén are among those who have made important recent contributions to the subject, in works already cited.[38, 39] Still more recently, Kurtén has devised an ingenious half-life method of making quantitative estimates of average rates in whole faunas—a method particularly well adapted to the kind of data now actually available.[40] With some other problems of rates, such as that of rate distributions within large taxa, a start has been made,[33] but recent progress has been disappointing because immediately usable data are inadequate, even though such data could be obtained and appropriate methods for analyzing them have already been devised. In all studies of evolutionary rates the greatest present impediment is the inaccuracy of estimates of absolute dates and lapses in time in years. Radioactivity dating is the best method available, but reliable long-half-life dates (for example, from uranium-lead) are still too few and too poorly tied in with fossil faunas, and reliable short-half-life dates (for example, from carbon-14) do not cover enough time. Some recent work, particularly with potassium-argon, does hold out hope for eventual solution of this problem.[41]

A still more complex whole field of primarily paleontological evolutionary problems concerns numerous intricately interrelated subjects: the rise of higher taxa and the evolutionary nature of higher categories; their duality of diversification and divergence; the occurrence of "explosive" episodes of diversification; the prevalence of parallel evolution throughout many high taxa and problems of polyphyly arising therefrom; patterns of early radiation in such groups as fishes, therapsids, and rodents. It is perhaps in this general field that vertebrate paleontology faces its most important problems of evolutionary theory and is making (or is capable of making) its greatest contributions to that subject. Even to exemplify these problems adequately and to cite the most important recent work on them would require another article longer than this one. Among other essential problems that can be barely mentioned here is that of extinction, about which a great deal has been written but very little can be said to be firmly known.

## PHILOSOPHY

The history of life and the processes of its evolution have a crucial bearing on philosophy—on our understanding of ourselves and of the universe in which we live. This is a subject that greatly transcends vertebrate paleontology, but here, too, vertebrate paleontology has, or should have, an essential role. Its area of main concern is a part of the history of life, and the most pertinent part, since it includes the ancestry of man from jawless fish onward. Vertebrate paleontology also participates, with other life sciences, in the elucidation of the processes by which we and the whole world of life evolved.

Among the great philosophical problems on which evolution and, therefore, also vertebrate paleontology bear are those of order in the universe, of utility or teleology, of progress, and of purpose or finality.[33,42] Decision on any of those problems must depend largely on what one considers to be the principal directive forces of evolution—whether natural selection (largely a resultant of interaction between organisms and environments), primary action of the environment itself, purely internal forces (especially gross mutations, irrespective of the environment), or metaphysical, nonmaterial, or divine impulses and finalities. One can hardly speak in an absolute sense of proving or disproving any of those views on evidence from vertebrate paleontology, but such evidence certainly bears on which views should be considered more and which less probable.

These questions are always approached on the basis of a priori postulates, seldom frankly stated, often nonscientific and sometimes even antiscientific. In the Soviet Union, purely political postulates forced support of Michurinism, a form of Neo-Lamarckism, even though most Russian biologists knew all the time that accumulated evidence has made that theory extremely improbable. Orthodox Christian, and particularly Roman Catholic, postulates are often, but not necessarily, construed as demanding vitalistic and finalistic control of evolution. Other views inevitably have their overt and covert postulates as well. The important thing is that those postulates should at least be consistent with and appropriate to the scientific approach—otherwise the contribution of vertebrate paleontology or any other life science to philosophy is negatived or stultified from the start. Unfortunately the postulates are not scientific in the most conspicuous recent contribution of a vertebrate paleontologist to this field: the mystical works of the late Teilhard de Chardin, a Jesuit priest, who departed from purely metaphysical postulates and rejected scientific evidence opposed to them.[43] A few vertebrate paleontologists have spoken for more strictly scientific postulation and inference, but most of them are publicly silent on philosophical questions and probably try to ignore them even in private. They may thereby be losing, by default, the opportunity to explore the most profound problems and values of their subject.

## REFERENCES AND NOTES

1. Although the number of vertebrate paleontologists in North America is still small, there has been a considerable percentage increase in recent years, and the number continues to rise slowly. In contrast, Lehman estimated in 1957 that the number of vertebrate paleontologists in Europe was then about the same as in 1900. Strictly speaking, there has never been a professional vertebrate paleontologist in Australia, and there is only a handful each in Asia, Africa, and South America.

2. Selection of topics and point of view are necessarily personal, but within the limited scope of this account I have tried to include the interests of others. I have done this largely on the broad basis of years of conversations, correspondence, and exchange of publications. In addition, I have sought explicit advice, in preparing this article, from a small sample of vertebrate paleontologists of varying interests and approaches, including some I might otherwise have missed. Among those who responded to that appeal are R. S. Bader, J. R. Beerbower, B. Kurtén, J. P. Lehman, M. C. McKenna, E. C. Olson, B. Patterson, A. S. Romer, D. E. Savage, B. Schaeffer, J. A. Shotwell, E. Simons, R. A. Stirton, and L. Van Valen. It has not been possible to include

all their suggestions, and they are not responsible for the necessary omissions.

3. For a strong but reasonable appeal for emphasis on the morphological approach, see J. P. Lehman, *Bull. muséum natl. d'hist. nat.* (Paris) **29**, 363 (1957).

4. See J. P. Lehman, *L'Évolution des vertébrés inférieurs* (Dunod, Paris, 1959); E. Jarvik, *Théories de l'évolution des vertébrés reconsidérées à la lumière des récentes découvertes sur les vertébrés inférieurs* (Masson, Paris, 1960).

5. F. C. Whitmore, Jr., *U.S. Geol. Surv. Prof. Papers No. 243-H* (1953).

6. R. Zangerl, *Evolution* **2**, 351 (1948).

7. Among many others, see A. S. Brink, *Palaeontol. Africa* **4**, 77 (1957); A. W. Crompton, *Proc. Zool. Soc. London* **130**, 183 (1958); E. C. Olson, *Evolution* **13**, 344 (1959); D. M. S. Watson and A. S. Romer, *Bull. Museum Comp. Zool.* **114**, 37 (1956). Much still unpublished work in this field was reported at Oxford in 1960.

8. The Brussels symposium was published in two volumes by the Flemish Academy of Science, Letters, and Fine Arts in 1961. See also B. Patterson, *Fieldiana. Geol.* **13**, 1 (1956).

9. E. H. Colbert and J. Imbrie, *Bull. Am. Museum Nat. Hist.* **110**, 399 (1956); E. C. Olson and R. L. Miller, *J. Paleontol.* **25**, 212 (1951).

10. E. C. Olson, *J. Geol.* **61**, 557 (1953); ——— and R. L. Miller, *Evolution* **5**, 325 (1951); ———, *Morphological Integration* (Univ. of Chicago Press, Chicago, 1958); B. Schaeffer, *Evolution* **10**, 201 (1956).

11. B. Schaeffer, *Am. J. Phys. Anthropol.* **8**, 281 (1950).

12. On this and other topics discussed in this section, see G. G. Simpson, *Principles of Animal Taxonomy* (Columbia Univ. Press, New York, 1961); on the statistical principles involved, see G. G. Simpson, A. Roe, R. C. Lewontin, *Quantitative Zoology* (Harcourt, Brace, New York, 1960).

13. E. C. Olson, *J. Geol.* **65**, 309 (1957).

14. J. A. Shotwell, *Ecology* **39**, 271 (1958).

15. R. W. Wilson, *Univ. Kansas Publs., Paleontol. Contrib., Vertebrata* (1960).

16. For different viewpoints on the problem for Mammalia, see L.

Van Valen, *Evolution,* **13,** 304 (1960); C. A. Reed, *ibid.* **13,** 314 (1960); G. G. Simpson, *ibid.* **13,** 389 (1960).

17. Among numerous current workers on this subject are P. M. Butler, S. B. McDowell, Jr., M. C. McKenna, and B. Patterson. The most crucial work is not yet published.

18. A. E. Wood, *Evolution* **13,** 354 (1959).

19. J. H. Quinn, *Univ. Texas Publ. No. 5516* (1955). As a matter of principle Quinn used taxonomic methods unacceptable to many of his colleagues, and his conclusions have not been widely adopted, but they certainly indicate that the classic phylogeny of the Equidae must be changed in many details. M. F. Skinner is currently working intensively on this subject.

20. G. Haas, *Am. Museum Novitates, No. 1729* (1955). Further examples of still broader and in part new approaches to functional analysis of fossil (and recent) skeletons are provided by R. J. G. Savage, *Proc. Zool. Soc. London* **129,** 151 (1957); J. M. Smith and R. J. G. Savage, *School Sci. Rev.* **40,** 289 (1959).

21. F. E. Peabody, *Univ. Calif. (Berkeley) Publs. Zoöl.* **63,** 1 (1959).

22. N. Hotton III, *Evolution,* **13,** 99 (1959).

23. A. S. Romer, in *Robert Broom Commemorative Volume* (Royal Society of South Africa, Rondebosch, 1948), p. 45.

24. P. M. Butler, *Proc. Zool. Soc. London* **B109,** 1 (1939).

25. B. Kurtén, *Acta Zool. Fennica,* **1953,** No. 76 (1953).

26. M. C. McKenna, *Univ. Calif. (Berkeley) Publs. Geol. Sciences* **37,** 1 (1960).

27. E. C. Olson, *Evolution* **6,** 181 (1952); *Fieldiana. Geol.* **10,** 397 (1958).

28. C. W. Hibbard, *Michigan Acad. Sci. Rept. 1959–60* (1960), p. 5.

29. J. A. Shotwell, *Evolution* **12,** 451 (1958).

30. G. G. Simpson, *Bull. Geol. Soc. Am.* **58,** 613 (1947); *Am. Scientist* **38,** 361 (1950); *Evolution and Geography* (Oregon State System of Higher Education, Eugene, 1953).

31. ———, *Am. J. Sci.* **258,** 300 (1960).

32. P. J. Darlington, *Zoogeography* (Wiley, New York, 1957).

33. On this section in general, see G. G. Simpson, *Major Features of Evolution* (Columbia Univ. Press, New York, 1953); G. G. Simp-

son, in *Evolution after Darwin,* S. Tax, Ed. (Univ. of Chicago Press, Chicago, 1960), vol. 1, p. 117.

34. Although not a paleontologist, Rensch has become the authority on "Cope's law"; see B. Rensch, *Evolution above the Species Level* (Columbia Univ. Press, New York, 1960).

35. The eponyms of all these "laws" are inappropriate; other workers had expressed them in one form or another before they were advanced by Dollo, Cope, or Williston.

36. W. K. Gregory, *Evolution Emerging* (Macmillan, New York, 1951).

37. E. C. Olson, in *Evolution after Darwin,* S. Tax, Ed. (Univ. of Chicago Press, Chicago, 1960), vol. 1, p. 523.

38. R. S. Bader, *Evolution* **9,** 119 (1955); ———, *Quart. J. Florida Acad. Sci.* **19,** 14 (1956); ——— and J. S. Hall, *Evolution* **14,** 8 (1960).

39. B. Kurtén, *Acta Zool. Fennica* **1958,** No. 95 (1958).

40. ———. *Soc. Sci. Fennica, Commentationes Biol.* **21,** No. 4 (1959); **22,** No. 5 (1960).

41. D. E. Savage, G. H. Curtis, J. F. Evernden, *Bull. Geol. Soc. Am.* **71,** 1966 (1960).

42. G. G. Simpson, *The Meaning of Evolution* (Yale Univ. Press, New Haven, Conn., 1949).

43. P. Teilhard de Chardin, *The Phenomenon of Man* (Harper, New York, 1959). The conclusion that this is not, as claimed, a "scientific treatise" is supported by G. G. Simpson [*Sci. American* **202,** 201 (1960)].

• • •

# PART 4

*This essay constitutes, as its title implies, the very heart of the book. It forms an extended survey of mammalian evolution and its relationship to geographical and geological change and stability. The appearance of various mammalian orders, families, genera and species, their movement about the globe, and, in some cases, their disappearance are outlined and commented upon. Earth history is examined in the light of paleontological discovery, and both the formation and changes in relationship of the various land areas are critically reviewed.*

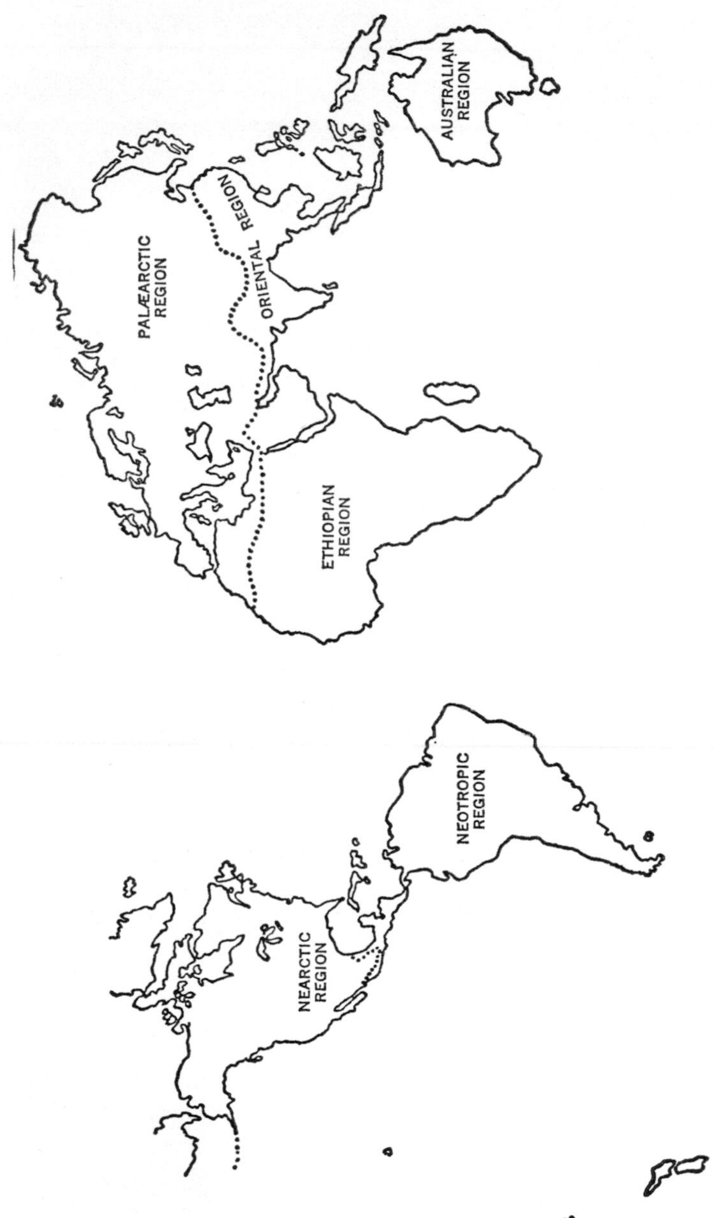


Fig. 11. The zoogeographical regions of the world. This is the arrangement as proposed by W. L. and P. L. Sclater in 1899.

• • •

# Evolution and Geography

## 1. INTRODUCTION TO BIOGEOGRAPHY

### the study of biogeography

It is an old and commonplace observation that each kind of animal or plant occurs in a particular area and not everywhere. Similarly, everyone knows that every region of the earth has its own association of animals and plants. This life-association always differs from one place to another. The differences may be slight or may be radical, but floras and faunas are never quite the same in two places. Pouched mammals (marsupials) and eucalyptus trees are characteristic of Australia, although not wholly confined to it, and the native animals and plants of, say, western Europe are completely different from those of Australia. The cold, dark depths of the sea are inhabited by myriad creatures and so are the windswept mountain tops, but there is no one kind of living thing that can live in both of those places. Living things have their own geography: that is the subject of *biogeography*.

The first approach to the study of biogeography is simple observation. The basic data of the science are the facts of distribution and association, answers to the question, "What lives where?"

Primitive hunters must have had sound knowledge of such facts for the animals and plants of practical importance to them. The wider intellectual curiosity of philosophers and travelers in ancient civilizations achieved a foreshadowing of biogeography, as of so many other sciences. The Greeks and Romans imagined that distant regions were the haunts of fabulous, nonexistent creatures, but they also knew that real bears and boars roamed the cool northern forests and that real lions and elephants were to be found in warmer, southern regions. Although a tremendous amount of detail still remains to be filled in today, the explorers and naturalists of the 19th century compiled the most essential facts about the distribution of living things throughout the world.

The mere compilation of facts poses questions rather than answering them. The aim of any science is not only to describe but also to interpret and, as far as possible, to explain its observations. When this attitude is applied to biogeography, it becomes evident that there are different sorts of observations to be explained. First, the flora and fauna, the *biota,* of any one place consist of particular species of plants and animals interacting with each other and with their geographic environment. In Oregon, for instance, the organisms of the seashore and those of the mountains are characteristically different from each other although the distance between them may be small. The differences are mainly environmental and their study is ecological. On faraway seashores and in more distant mountains, environments closely similar to those in Oregon are found and they are occupied by biotas living and interacting in much the same ways. Nevertheless they may be composed of completely different species. Here are differences that are not primarily or exclusively ecological but that are in some stricter sense *geographical.*

The descriptive studies of the 19th century culminated in a number of broad generalizations. As regards land mammals, to which the present essay is mainly devoted, the most important generalization was a subdivision of the land areas of the world into zoogeographic regions by, among others, the Sclaters (1899, see References at end of this essay) and Lydekker (1896). A usual arrangement of the major regions is shown in Fig. 11. Each region has a broadly characteristic mammalian fauna different in important ways from any other region. The differences between the regions are only in part ecological; they are more basically geographical.

Regional subdivision of faunas is still description and not explanation, even though it is on a more or less high level of generalization. To state that the Neotropical Region, for instance, is characterized by edentates (armadillos, anteaters, and sloths), by New World monkeys, by guinea pigs and their relatives, and so on, does not help to explain why that is so. Later work along those lines of classical zoogeography has not been particularly rewarding. It has been concerned in part with the exact placing of the boundaries of faunal regions, whereas sharp and precisely placeable lines between the regions are not really present in nature. In other part, it has involved rearrangement of lesser geographic subdivisions within the main regions, subdivisions that are more a matter of convenience than of fact or that are better approached from an ecological than from a strictly geographical viewpoint. Thus, recent summaries of descriptive zoogeography, such as that of de Beaufort (1951), although they add some interesting details, do not substantially advance understanding beyond that of the 1890's.

The comparative sterility of the descriptive geographic approach has led many 20th-century students to turn to ecological zoogeography. They have been concerned not so much with regional relationships among faunas as with environmental relationships. That approach has, indeed, been highly fertile, and great strides have been and are now being made, as well exemplified in the review by Hesse, Allee, and Schmidt (1951).

Both the geographical distribution and the ecological relationships of animals are outcomes of evolution. That is the basis for another approach to zoogeography, the *historical* approach. Where animals are and what they do there are results of historical processes and events. An understanding of historical zoogeography is therefore the one way in which a true explanation of the observed facts of zoogeography can be achieved. Lydekker (1896) already understood that point when he called his book *A Geographical*

*History of Mammals.* His own success in explaining the geography of mammals was markedly limited by the then scanty knowledge of both processes and events in the history of that group. Since then, much progress has been made, especially by paleontologists, which is quite natural because paleontologists are most concerned with historical concepts. Among the early landmarks of that progress were Osborn's *The Age of Mammals* (1910), which assembled data on pertinent historical events, and Matthew's *Climate and Evolution* (1915), which tackled still more complex problems of theoretical interpretation of processes. Many special studies have been made, and the subject has greatly advanced. Even now, however, there is available no adequate treatment of the field of historical biogeography, either in general or for a particular group such as the mammals. (The present essay is, of course, no such treatment; although it tries to indicate briefly a few of the many topics that should be covered.) *

## aims, methods, and materials

Evolutionary change may be considered under three aspects, each of which has its own bearings on biogeography. There are, *first,* the processes of biological change within each of the various lineages of organisms. Any such change alters in some degree the interactions of the organisms with other organisms, with, in general, the world around them or their whole environment. Hence it alters the role of the organisms in the natural community, and there are, *second,* changes in communities, biotas, or biocenoses. The composition of the biota as a whole changes not only because of biological change in its members but also because of the extinction or emigration of some groups and the introduction of others. The latter factors involve, *third,* historical changes in the geographic distribution of groups of organisms. The composition and the total functioning of a biota at any one place and time are the total result

* Since these lines were written, an excellent general study has appeared (Darlington, 1957). There is, however, no significant duplication with the present essay.

of these three inextricably linked kinds of historical processes. The aim of historical biology is to understand these processes and to trace their changing results through time. Insofar as geographical changes are involved, the subject is historical biogeography.

The evolutionary processes have been operative for a very long time. Present estimates of the age of the earth are on the order of three billion years, and life may well have existed on it for two billion years or so. Such is the time scale of the whole history of life, but the more limited aim of interpreting the geography of mammals requires a somewhat less incredibly long scale (Fig. 12). Mammals arose as such about 150–175 million years ago, fairly early in the Age of Reptiles. The mammals remained small and obscure while the reptiles, especially the dinosaurs, were dominant. Mammals began to rise to dominance in their turn, and hence ushered in the Age of Mammals, about 75 million years ago. Most of the events reflected in the present geography of mammals have occurred since that time, and more remote history is of no great significance for this particular subject. (Just the same, it should be remembered that the present condition of the earth and its life is the result of the *whole* history of this planet and not only of its later parts.)

There has always been an interplay of biological change, evolution in the usual sense of the word, and of changes in the physical environment, which are broadly evolution, also, but geographical rather than biological evolution. The rise of a mountain range where once was a lowland or the incursion of a sea where once was dry land is a historical geographic event that obliterates one kind of environment and replaces it by another. Changes like those are necessarily accompanied by changes in the biotas occupying such regions. The linking of two formerly separated regions by a practicable migration route makes possible geographic movements of many kinds of organisms. These and other considerations make it evident that the history of life can be understood only against the background of the history of the surface of the earth. The direct study of earth history involves mostly the rocks of the earth's crust. The nature and sequence of those rocks are the physical records of geographic events. That is a part of the science of geology, which

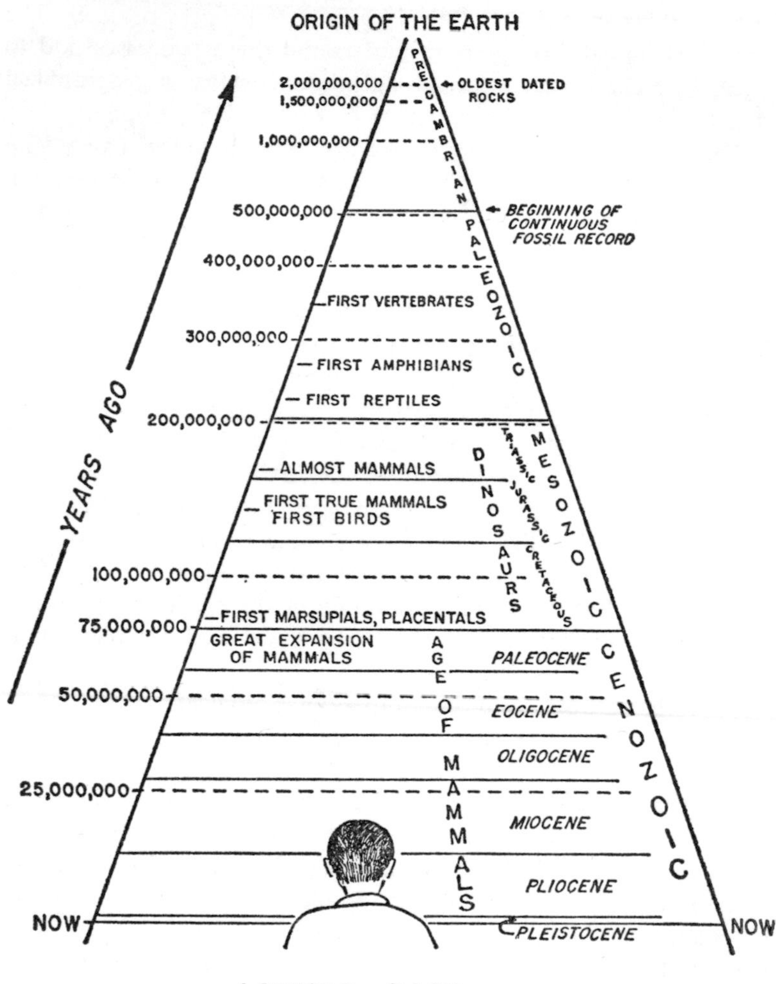


Fig. 12. Looking back down the road of time. Geological time is seen in perspective, with approximate dates in years before the present to the left and technical geological names for subdivisions of time to the right. The dates of some important events in the history of the backboned animals (vertebrates) are indicated.

thus provides background for historical biogeography, but the two subjects cannot be separated. Each casts essential light on the other.

The direct historical records for biogeography are fossils. The data are the occurrence of a particular sort of organism (preserved as a fossil, the taxonomic datum) at a particular time (defined by its place in the geological sequence, Fig. 12, the time datum) and at a particular place (the basic geographical datum). If such data are fairly complete, the historical events can be followed with considerable objectivity and little inference. In fact the fossil record is full of gaps and the direct historical record is never anything like complete. For some groups of animals, however, known fossils are sufficiently abundant and sufficiently distributed in time and space so that the broad outlines, at least, of the history can be followed with considerable assurance. The mammals are such a group.

If the fossil record of a group of organisms is poor or lacking, then its geographical history must be reconstructed (if at all) by inference from present conditions. In other words, only the result of a long sequence of events is known and the problem is to reconstruct the events from their result. That is always a hazardous and uncertain procedure. Sometimes it seems downright impossible, and we may as well admit that attempts to give historical explanations for the present geography of certain groups of plants or animals have little or no value. Yet some inferences can be made with fair probability provided that we can develop clear understanding of general principles effective in historical biogeography. The way to discover such principles is by study of groups that do have the best fossil records. Thus the historical biogeography of mammals is important not only for its own sake but also for the guidance it can give for inferences when dealing with organisms less well known as fossils.

## some historical principles

There is one tendency evident in the whole fossil record, taking into account all plants, all animals, or both together: throughout its history life has tended to expand, to include increasingly greater numbers of kinds of living things (Fig. 13). The tendency is not entirely regular. There have been times when life contracted rather than expanded, and particular groups of plants or animals have often contracted or become wholly extinct. Nevertheless the usual total tendency has been expansive. That tendency was also evident for the group (technically a class in taxonomy) of the mammals (Fig. 14). From their ancient and obscure beginnings, mammals expanded greatly through much of their history. In the last few

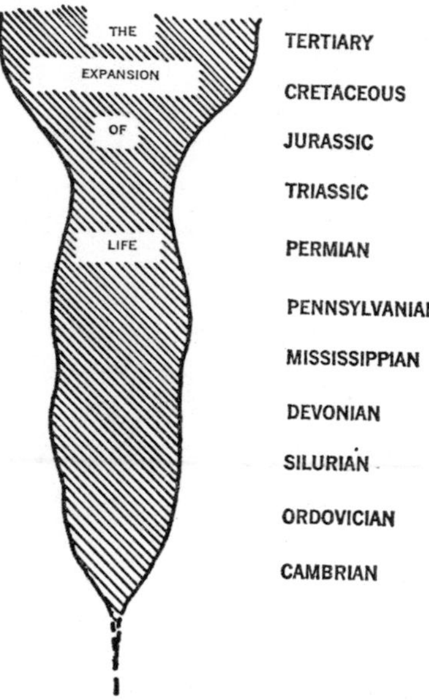


Fig. 13. The expansion of life. The width of the figure is approximately in proportion to the known diversity of organisms at various times in the past. The beginning of fairly continuous record, in the Cambrian, dates from about 500 million years ago.

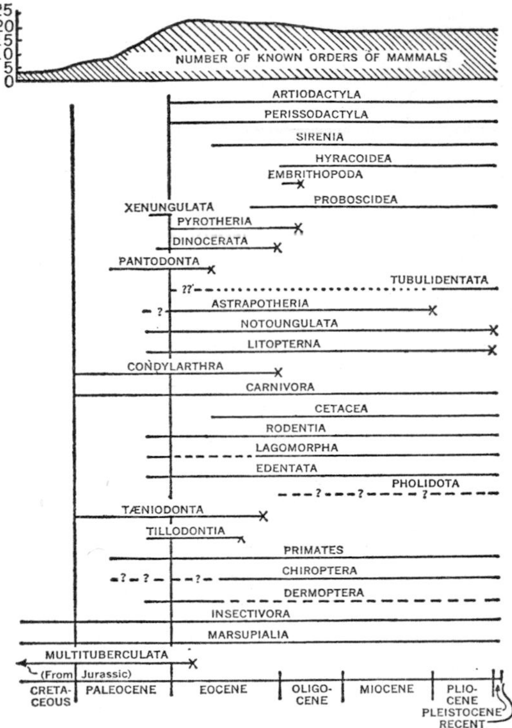


Fig. 14. Known records of the major groups, orders, of mammals during the Age of Mammals. The time scale runs from left to right. Note rapid increase in total orders known during the first epoch, Paleocene, of the Age of Mammals and then slight decline and stabilization.

million years they have contracted somewhat, but this contrary tendency is not yet strongly marked and the earlier great expansion is an important factor in the geographic spread of mammals.

Occupation of the environment is a factor underlying the tendency of living things to expand. Ordinarily two kinds of organisms playing the same role in nature or, so to speak, making their livings in the same way cannot long live together. Expansion of a group therefore cannot occur merely by an increase in the number of species making their living in the same way and in the same environment. Increase in diversity usually involves either the evolution of different ways of making a living or spread into new environments (or both). The first of those processes is strikingly exemplified in the phenomenon of adaptive radiation. In the late Cretaceous (see Fig. 12 for this and other geological time terms), the ancestors of most later mammals were small, shrewlike creatures all living in much the same way and therefore including relatively few species. By Eocene times their descendants in numerous different lines had

Fig. 15. How to make a living. Markedly different ways of life among the mammals had been established as early as the Eocene by adaptive radiation. That phenomenon is a basic factor in increasing and maintaining diversity in all large groups of animals.

diverged or radiated by evolutionary change adapting them to many different ways of life: some were aquatic, some amphibious, some terrestrial, some arboreal, and some aerial; some ate seeds, some leaves, some insects, some other mammals; some were large and some small—and so on, until a great many different ways of making a living were included (Fig. 15).

Also involved in such a picture is increasingly narrow speciali-

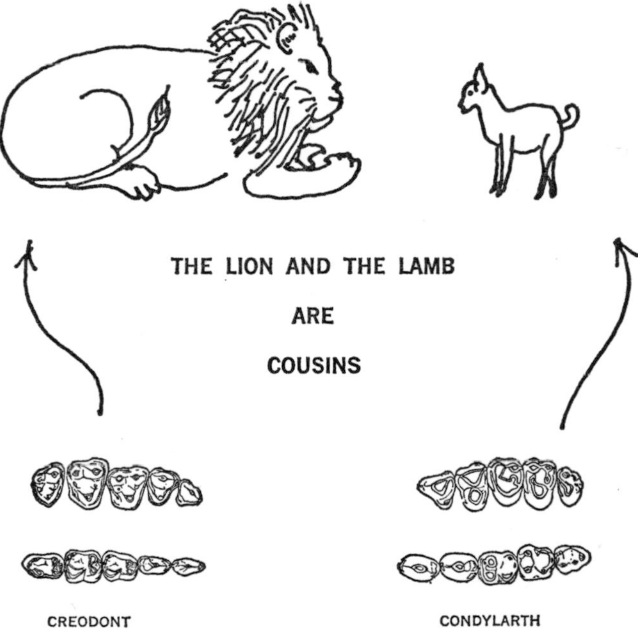


Fig. 16. An example of increasing specialization and divergence in the course of evolution. Primitive ancestors of carnivores and ungulates are represented by upper and lower teeth of a creodont and a condylarth, respectively. (The creodont teeth are from the right side, the condylarth teeth from the left.) Those ancestors were closely similar to each other in structure and habits, and evidently had little narrowing of food habits, being more or less omniverous. From them arose such diversely specialized forms as the strictly carnivorous lion and the strictly herbivorous lamb.

zation. For instance, many early mammals were evidently not very particular about what they ate. Almost any food that they could find and gulp down was eaten. Their utilization of it was probably not very efficient, but one way or another they got enough to keep going. Many of their descendants became more specialized: they could and did eat only one kind of food, which they utilized with increased efficiency. When each kind of animal is a specialist, there are of course more different kinds. You might say that animals tend to develop different and narrower trades, a contrast like that between the old-time laborer and the many kinds of trade specialists in modern industry (Fig. 16).

The concept that animals make their livings in different ways or follow different trades has consequences in the organization of natural communities, in which the activities of all organisms intermesh in complex ways. Green plants are primary producers, acquiring energy from the sun and materials from soil and air. Various different kinds of herbivorous animals eat different plants or different parts of the same plant. Different kinds of carnivorous animals eat the various kinds of herbivorous animals. Organisms of decay consume dead plants and animals and return their materials to soil and air. (The actual interrelationships may be far more complex than this abbreviated example.) Such is a balanced biota, in which there is a large but definite number of different roles or trades each of which can be followed by one kind of plant or animal.

Another general historical tendency is to fill and to keep filled all the roles of a biota, to keep the community full and in balance. If a species with a definite role disappears for any reason, there is a tendency—not invariable but usual—for some other species from within the community or from outside to take over the role. Hence another frequent phenomenon in the evolution of faunas: the replacement of one group of animals by another. Sometimes replacement is delayed and a role remains open for some time, even occasionally for millions of years. More often the replacement is rapid and frequently by competition; the disappearance of one kind of animal occurs because another kind takes over its role. The possible roles within a community also usually evolve and change, but even if they do not, there is likely to be continuous change in the kinds of animals playing the various roles. The balance of a balanced community is not static but is fluidly dynamic as followed historically.

The presence in one community of two or more kinds of animals with roles similar in some essential way is almost always temporary. Sooner or later one kind takes over the role and the other acquires a different role, emigrates, or becomes extinct. The unbalancing of a community by duplication of roles means that somehow more species are present than could normally evolve or continue to live in the given environment. Such a situation means that some species has invaded the community (and its environment) from elsewhere; it is a consequence of the migration of species into new environments or more broadly of the interchange of species between different faunal regions. Such events have occurred over and over again in the history of life in general and of mammals in particular. Some striking examples will be given later in this essay.

(Some pertinent evolutionary principles are more fully discussed in Simpson, 1949 b; the functional organization and evolution of communities are included in Allee, Emerson, Park, Park and Schmidt, 1949.)

## 2. ISOLATION AND MIGRATION

### barriers, parallel radiations, and convergence

The number and nature of different kinds of organisms are not restricted to the roles possible in any one community or geographic area. Environments differ greatly from community to community and from place to place. Therefore the possible roles also differ, and taking the earth as a whole their number is enormous. So much is fairly obvious. There is another factor that makes it possible for different kinds of animals to play essentially the same roles and therefore for the total number of species at any one time to be greater than the total number of ecological roles.

If animals can move freely from one place to another, then the tendency is for the same species to play the same role in both places. If, however, there is a barrier to movement between the two places, then it is more common than not for different animals to have more or less similar roles in the two. Such pairs of species are called *vicarious,* because one takes the place of the other in its particular community. They characterize strictly geographic differences between faunas that live in similar environments and are not markedly different ecologically. The origin and persistence of such differences depends on the existence of a geographically localized barrier of some sort.

Barriers are of many different kinds. For a lowland animal, a mountain range is a formidable barrier. For a steppe animal, a dense forest is a barrier. For a species adapted to warm water, a cold current is an effective barrier. For land mammals, my special topic here, the most important barriers are wide bodies of water. The broad outlines of the historical geography of mammals are concerned mainly with the development of the faunas of the various continents, and the barriers most important for this study are the stretches of sea that have at different times separated one continent from another. The New World is now completely separated from the Old by such barriers although, as will later be stressed, this has not always been so and is, indeed, historically unusual. Australia is isolated by sea barriers from all other continents, and that isolation is of long standing. South America is not now fully isolated from North America, but it was through most of the Age of Mammals.

Large and environmentally varied land areas have been the scenes of extensive adaptive radiation among land mammals. When such an area is surrounded by sea barriers, its adaptive radiation proceeds in isolation, or nearly so, independently from radiation that may be going on simultaneously in other regions. Thus through the Age of Mammals Australia and South America, island continents, had adaptive radiations separate from each other and from the complex radiation in Africa, Eurasia, and North America—continents repeatedly and lengthily connected with each other during this era. In each of the isolated, parallel radiations there was a tendency for similar roles to be occupied by adaptive evolution, but the ancestral forms were generally different in the different regions and the independent evolutionary sequences tended to be somewhat different in any case. Thus it happened that mammals of different origin and history developed closely similar ecological roles in Australia, South America, and the rest of the terrestrial world. There was widespread evolution of vicarious forms, functionally similar but only distantly related. That phenomenon of *convergent* evolution is especially striking in the case of parallel continental adaptive radiation.

Predaceous, doglike carnivores are striking examples of convergent evolution. In Australia there evolved the so-called Tasmanian wolf, not a wolf at all but a pouched mammal, a marsupial, related to our opossum. In South America there were also wolflike marsupial carnivores, similar and related to those of Australia but nevertheless of quite distinct ancestry. In Africa, Eurasia, and North America there were true wolves and other members of the dog family, similar in habits and appearance to the marsupial "wolves" of Australia and South America, but in blood relationship actually closer to ourselves than to those convergent and ecologically similar marsupials. (Fig. 17.) In both Australia and South America there were in fact whole series of animals convergent to many diverse groups on other continents.

Such events produce in different regions extensive duplication of adaptive types or ecological roles, which arise and persist as long as the duplicating groups do not come into contact. If they do come into contact by spread of animals from one region to another, the duplication is eventually eliminated. Thus the marsupial "wolves" (along with many other duplicating groups) became extinct in South America when true dogs invaded from North America, and the marsupial "wolves" of Australia similarly became extinct when dogs were introduced from Asia by early man. (A few marsupial

Fig. 17. Convergent carnivores that evolved in independent adaptive radiations on three different land masses. *A,* the true wolf of Eurasia and North America. *B,* the marsupial or Tasmanian "wolf" of Australia and Tasmania. *C,* an extinct marsupial (a borhyaenid) of South America (the coat pattern is entirely hypothetical).

"wolves" may still survive on the island of Tasmania, where dogs were of later introduction.)

### paths of faunal interchange

Of all faunal changes the most radical are those produced by the spread of animals from one region to another, the most basic phenomenon of dynamic or historical biogeography. Barriers, which impede freedom of movement, and migration or expansion routes, which promote it, are thus the basic geographic factors in the history of faunas. Freedom of movement and its restriction are relative. No two places have exactly the same environment, and any difference of environment is likely to be in some degree a deterrent to spread of animals from one place to another. Seldom if ever can it be said that there is absolutely no impediment to spread of a species or on the contrary that there is a barrier so strong that spread is absolutely impossible. It is all a matter of degree, of diverse probabilities. (On probabilities of dispersal see Simpson, 1952.)

The probability of spread of a group of animals from one region to another may have any level from nearly impossible to nearly certain, depending on the geographic and other environmental conditions between the two regions. Although any degree of probability may occur and no sharp distinctions are possible, it is convenient to consider three main sorts of paths of faunal interchange: *corridors, filters,* and *sweepstakes routes.* (These were so designated and were discussed at greater length in Simpson, 1940 a.)

A *corridor* is a route along which the spread of many or most of the animals of one region to another is probable. A typical corridor has long existed from western Europe across Asia into China. Such a varied and extended stretch of land presents some impediment to faunal interchange, and the fauna of, say, France is of course not exactly like that of northern China. Nevertheless these two faunas are decidedly similar, much more so, for example, than the French and central African faunas in spite of the fact that France is much closer to central Africa than to China. If the faunas of two regions are markedly different, as much so, for instance, as those of the Sclaters' zoogeographical regions (Fig. 11), you may be quite sure that an open corridor between them has not existed for some time.

A *filter* is a route across which spread of some animals is fairly probable but spread of others is definitely improbable. Hence some elements of a regional fauna expand readily across the filter and into another region, but other elements do not. The route is a semibarrier that permits parts of faunas to pass but filters out others.

(Of course this is still a matter of degree; a corridor usually filters out some animals, and a strong barrier does not necessarily hold back all animals.) A filter may be a desert, such as the Sahara and adjacent deserts, or a mountain range, such as the Himalayan system. Between different continents, a filter is generally a land bridge, an isthmian connection narrower and more specific in environmental conditions than a corridor and hence a stronger impediment to faunal interchange. That intercontinental land bridges do have strong filtering action, that they are *filter bridges,* is one of the most important conclusions from the study of faunal interchanges. The

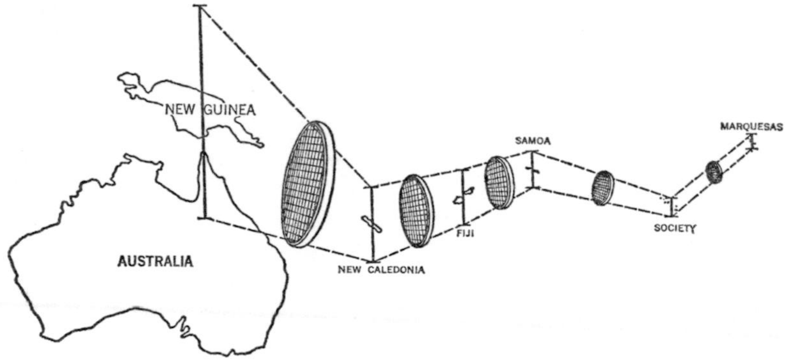


Fig. 18. Dispersal along a sweepstakes route. A group of weevils (Cryptorhynchinae) has island-hopped from west to east. The vertical bars are proportional in length to the diversity (number of genera) of the group at each place. Clearly the group has been sifted out, fewer and fewer managing to follow each successive sweepstakes route. These insects are particularly good at sweepstakes dispersal. (Data from E. C. Zimmerman)

connection between North and South America is a filter bridge now in existence, of which the past action and present consequences can be analyzed in detail. (See Essay 6, this volume, "History of the Fauna of Latin America.")

At the other end of the scale from a corridor, a *sweepstakes route* is one across which spread is highly improbable for most or all animals but does occur for some. In other words, a sweepstakes route is a formidable barrier that is nevertheless occasionally crossed. The implication of the term is that as in a lottery or sweepstakes the odds against winning are enormous but nevertheless someone does win. Another point is the element, apparent at least, of chance in following a sweepstakes route. Where a corridor or filter exists, most or all of the groups adaptively capable of following the route will do so rather promptly. With a sweepstakes route, probabilities are so much against all groups that crossing may be long delayed. What groups do, in fact, cross, which do so first, and when they do so seem to be largely matters of chance, determined almost at random. (Spread along a sweepstakes route is often called *waif dispersal.*) (See Fig. 18.)

For land animals the most obvious and important sweepstakes routes involve spread across channels, straits, or still wider sea barriers. Such dispersal explains how land animals have reached islands and island continents, and its circumstances clear up some striking anomalies in the faunal histories of such lands. Many zoogeographers used to assume (and a few still do) that if land animals are found on an island, such as Madagascar or Hawaii, or on an island continent, such as Australia, they must have reached there by continuous land, across a filter bridge, at least, if not a land corridor. It is now clear that this is not necessarily so and that, in fact, sweepstakes dispersal has often occurred during the long span of geological time. Moreover, it has become clear that, when the whole fauna is taken into consideration, the land faunas of some islands cannot be explained by land connections and that some, at least, of the ancestral forms must have followed a sweepstakes route. Some of the criteria, not necessarily infallible but always highly suggestive, are as follows:

| Land Bridge | Sweepstakes Route |
| --- | --- |
| Generally serves for spread of animals in both directions. | May permit spread in both directions but often does so in one direction, only. |
| Serves for spread of balanced faunas to unoccupied areas, and | Commonly serves for spread of impoverished, unbalanced faunas, |

| | |
|---|---|
| tends to maintain full and balanced faunas on both of the areas connected. | and permits maintenance of such faunas on an isolated land area. |
| Is usually crossed by various different groups at the same time. | Is usually followed by one group at a time. |
| Is relatively determinate. Most or all groups that can cross do so, and they tend to cross soon after the route becomes available to them. | Is relatively random or indeterminate. Groups that might cross do not necessarily do so; crossings may be long delayed and are scattered through time; and the sequence seems to depend in part on chance. |

It was, for example, long disputed how the island of Madagascar acquired its peculiar fauna of land mammals. Zoogeographers used to postulate a land connection with Africa, or right across the Indian Ocean from Africa to India via Madagascar. Application of the foregoing criteria shows that the ancestral Malagasy mammals can only have come by a sweepstakes route. (See Matthew, 1915; Simpson, 1940 a; Millot, 1952.) Probably the most striking single example of sweepstakes dispersal (although it includes no mammals) is that of the Hawaiian Islands, tremendously isolated by sea barriers and never connected to any other land. (A few students

ODDS IN THE HAWAIIAN SWEEPSTAKES *

| *Groups* | *Endemics* | *Estimated number of ancestral (invading) species* | *Colonizations per 100,000 years* | *Odds per year* |
|---|---|---|---|---|
| Land mammals | 0 | 0 | 0 | Less than 1 to 5,000,000 |
| Land birds | 70 | 15 | 0.3 | 1 to 333,333 |
| Insects | 3,722 | 250 | 5 | 1 to 20,000 |
| Land snails | 1,061 | 25 | 0.5 | 1 to 200,000 |
| Seed plants | 1,633 | 270 | 5.4 | 1 to 18,518 |

* The data are taken from Zimmerman (1948), who estimates the age of the Hawaiian Islands as five million years. Some authorities consider the islands as much older, which would make the demonstrated odds for colonization still smaller.

have disputed that point, but it is fair to say that they were certainly wrong.) In spite of the continuous presence of maximal barriers, the islands have developed a rich land flora and fauna, but the native biota is highly peculiar and strongly unbalanced. All ancestral forms came by sweepstakes routes, and the high odds involved can be (very roughly) calculated.

### concomitants of faunal interchange

When faunal interchange occurs between two regions, new elements are introduced into the faunas. Extensive, even radical readjustments and evolutionary changes may occur as concomitants of such a zoogeographic event, comparatively simple in itself. Interchanges constantly occur among local faunas of a single continent. Most striking and most significant on a broad scale are faunal interchanges between two continents, which have also occurred repeatedly during the Age of Mammals. Early in the history, especially in the Paleocene, basic adaptive radiation was still in progress, and in any given region there were usually still possible ecological roles not yet actually played by mammals present in the region. Newcomers, evolved elsewhere and spreading geographically, were commonly of new adaptive types that fitted into the regional fauna without essential duplication. The result then was mostly enrichment of the fauna, increase in its diversity and in its occupation of the complex environment. Such enrichment is the dominant factor in the Paleocene history of the mammalian faunas of North America, the only continent where a fairly continuous sequence of faunas from early to late Paleocene is yet known.

By Eocene times Eurasia, North America, and South America at least, and probably all the continents had rich, essentially full and balanced mammalian faunas. Even without introduction of new groups such faunas continue to change because environments change and because there is a tendency for specialization and subdivision of ecological roles, as already mentioned. In fact, however, new groups did eventually, and in some cases repeatedly, spread into continental areas in which the environments were already saturated, so to speak, by groups of native mammals. Even so, the new groups were sometimes so distinctive ecologically that they fitted into unoccupied or only partially occupied roles or niches, as the ecologists say. Usually, however, extensive invasions produced considerable duplication of roles. To continue the metaphor, the environment then became supersaturated and in due course something had to crystallize out—that is, one or another of the competing groups became extinct. The fauna became unbalanced not by deficiency, as in the case of the West Indies, for example, where there were no native carnivores, but by excess. Any major interchange between continents is followed by a period of readjustment during which a new balance with altered faunal composition is achieved.

A long major episode of faunal excess with subsequent rebalancing occurred from latest Paleocene to latest Eocene in North America (see Fig. 24 on a later page). In that case the sources of most of the invading animals have not been surely identified, although they probably came from the Old World. A rather similar episode occurred when there was a great interchange of mammals between North and South America in the late Pliocene and the Pleistocene. The sources of the groups involved are known in this example, which can be analyzed in detail, as shown in the table below. The first table clearly reflects the great increase in diversity at the height of the interchange and subsequent re-establishment of balance at or even below previous levels of diversity, with marked changes in faunal composition especially in South America. Further analysis of this particular example shows that there was no particular correlation between spread and extinction, but that there was a strong correlation between source, spread, and survival. North American groups were much more successful than South American, probably because they were already the selected survivors of a long series of intermigrations with Eurasia while the South American mammals had been evolving in isolation. More North American than South American mammals succeeded in spreading to the other continent. More North American mammals survived the great extinction of the Pleistocene and early Recent. Yet, oddly enough, as the second table, "Faunal Interchange Between the Americas," shows, there is no significant correlation between migration and survival: about the same proportion of stay-at-homes as of migrants survived. (The example is more fully discussed in Simpson, 1950.)

FAMILIES OF LAND MAMMALS AT VARIOUS TIMES IN NORTH AND SOUTH AMERICA

South America

| | *Total* | *Autochthons* | *From North America* |
|---|---|---|---|
| Recent | 30 | 16 | 14 |
| Pleistocene | 36 | 23 | 13 |
| Mid-Pliocene | 25 | 24 | 1 |
| Mid-Miocene | 23 | 23 | 0 |

North America

| | *Total* | *Holarctic Autochthons* | *From South America* |
|---|---|---|---|
| Recent | 23 | 20 | 3 |
| Pleistocene | 34 | 26 | 8 |
| Mid-Pliocene | 27 | 26 | 1 |
| Mid-Miocene | 27 | 27 | 0 |

FAUNAL INTERCHANGE BETWEEN THE AMERICAS *

| *Number of families that:* | *From South America* | *From North America* |
|---|---|---|
| Migrated | 8 | 16 |
| Did not migrate | 17 | 11 |
| Ratios | .5 | 1.5 |
| Surviving | 16 | 21 |
| Extinct | 9 | 6 |
| Ratios | 1.8 | 3.5 |

* The relationships between geographic origin, migration, and survival of families of land mammals in faunal interchange between North and South America. Northern types both traveled more and were tougher.

## 3. THE COMPOSITION OF MAMMALIAN FAUNAS

### analysis of faunal composition

A *fauna* is an exceedingly complex aggregation. The fauna of any one area is made up of numerous species which have evolved from diverse ancestral groups, which interact with each other in various ways, which (either as such or in ancestral forms) have been in the region for different lengths of time, which have come from different geographic sources, and which have at present different relationships to species existing in other regions. The full analysis of a fauna would therefore include the following, at least:

1. Systematic classification of all groups present. (Such a classification also implies consideration of the ancestry of each group and of phylogenetic relationships among the groups.)
2. Ecological characteristics of each group and ecological relationships among all groups. (This involves not only individual physiology, adaptive characteristics, and correlation with environmental conditions but also the intricate cycles of transfer of energy and materials in communities, relative abundance and population density and cycles, and many other points.)
3. Antiquity of each group within the region.
4. Geographic source of each group. (Even though a group as such may have evolved in the region, its ancestors are likely to have come from elsewhere—a point connected with that of antiquity in the region.)
5. Current geographic affinities of each group. (That involves mainly the geographic distribution of the various categories of classification of members of the fauna.)

Each of these different lines of analysis may be a static description of present conditions (or those at any one time in the past), or it may be a dynamically historical study of changes in faunal composition through time. In any case, study begins with some sort of systematic classification of members of faunas. Ecological animal geography is concerned mainly with correlation of adaptive status with geographically definable environments. Although this, too, must be put on a historical basis if it is to be fully understood, relatively little work has yet been done on ecological changes of communities through really long periods of time. (For short periods there are, however, some excellent studies.)

Classical zoogeography was concerned almost entirely with current geographical affinities. Historical zoogeography has dealt, and still deals, with changes in such affinities through time (for an example see Fig. 32 on a later page), but it is more particularly concerned with geographic sources. That study turns out also to require consideration of regional antiquity.

## antiquity, source, and geographical affinities

"What is a native animal?" is an apparently simple question that must be answered if the origins of any fauna are to be considered. As so often happens with simple questions, the answer is complicated. It depends on how long a group of animals must have been in a region to be considered native. In fact the dichotomy "native-not native" is not particularly enlightening. The important thing is *how* native, or in other words how long the ancestry of the group has been in the region. A somewhat indirect but practical way to formalize the question and its answer in meaningful terms is to consider the matter in terms of classification, to discuss the "nativeness" not only of small units of classification, especially the species, but also of increasingly broader groups such as the genus or the family. If a family can be shown to have arisen in a given region, then that is the most ancient source or ancestral home of all species in the family, and similarly, usually at less remote times, for a genus and all its species. For clarity it is further necessary to distinguish between a group that is merely native to a region—that is, lives there naturally and not by human introduction or occasional straying—and a group that is autochthonous—that is, originated by evolution in the stated region.

The perhaps abstruse idea of different degrees of nativeness for different units or levels of classification may be clarified by the example in Fig. 19. The deer family, the Cervidae, arose (it is probable) in temperate Eurasia. The family is thus not autochthonous in either North or South America. A particular genus of the family, *Odocoileus,* evolved in North America from an ancestry that earlier spread from Asia to North America. Hence that genus, which includes our whitetails and mule deer, is autochthonous in

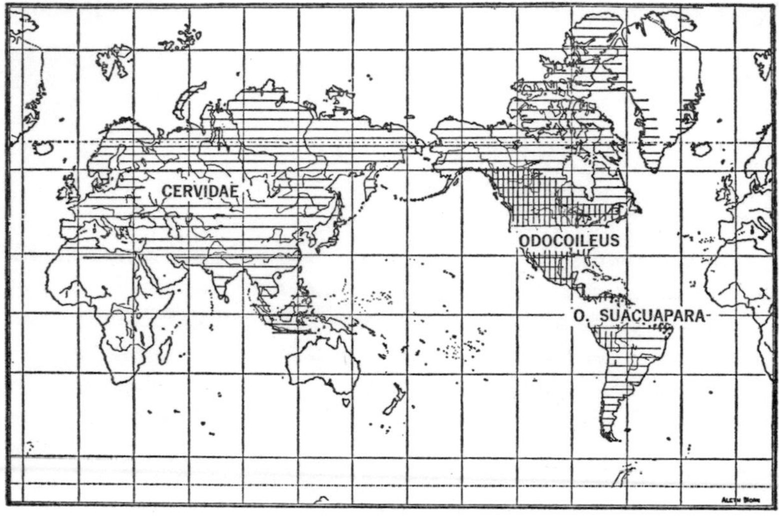


Fig. 19. Present distribution and geographic origin of the deer family and including lesser groups. The family Cervidae originated on the Eurasian land mass marked with its name and now occurs throughout the regions with horizontal cross-hatching. The genus Odocoileus (which includes the common Virginia and mule deer) originated in the general region marked with that name and now occurs throughout the vertically ruled area. The species Odocoileus *suacuapara* arose in the area indicated by dots, to which it is now confined.

North America, although its family is not. *Odocoileus,* is not autochthonous in South America, but in South America there is a species of that genus, *Odocoileus suacuapara,* which arose there and is therefore autochthonous. The immediate ancestors of that species came from North America, where the genus is autochthonous, and more distant ancestors from Eurasia, where the family is autochthonous.

## ANALYSIS OF THE RECENT NEARCTIC LAND MAMMAL FAUNA

AGE IN NEARCTIC (KNOWN AGE FROM FOSSILS):

| | *Cretaceous* | *Paleocene* | *Eocene* | *Oligocene* | *Miocene* | *Pliocene* | *Pleistocene* | *Recent* |
|---|---|---|---|---|---|---|---|---|
| Families: No. | 1 | 0 | 4 | 7 | 6 | 4 | 2 | 0 |
| % | 4 | 0 | 17 | 29 | 25 | 17 | 8 | 0 |
| Genera: No. | 0 | 0 | 0 | 0 | 5 | 27 | 37 | 10 |
| % | 0 | 0 | 0 | 0 | 6 | 34 | 47 | 13 |

PRESENT GEOGRAPHIC RELATIONS:

| | *Endemic in Nearctic* | *Also Neotropical* | *Also Asian* | *Also European* | *Also Ethopian* |
|---|---|---|---|---|---|
| Families: No. | 3 | 13 | 15 | 15 | 7 |
| % | 12 | 54 | 62 | 62 | 29 |
| Genera: No. | 36 | 18 | 29 | 24 | 3 |
| % | 46 | 23 | 37 | 30 | 4 |

MOST LIKELY GEOGRAPHIC ORIGIN:

| | *Autochthonous in Nearctic* | *From South America* | *From Eurasia* | *Either autochthonous or from Eurasia* |
|---|---|---|---|---|
| Families: No. | 6 | 2 | 9 | 7 |
| % | 25 | 8 | 38 | 29 |
| Genera: No. | 49 | 3 | 12 | 15 |
| % | 62 | 4 | 15 | 19 |

The example of the deer happens to be a particularly simple one zoogeographically because each unit of classification still occurs in the region where it is autochthonous. That is not necessarily so in other cases. The camel family, for instance, was autochthonous in North America where there are now no native camels. The family Camelidae now occurs in the Palaearctic and Neotropical Regions, an odd zoogeographic resemblance between distant parts of the world—but it was native to the Nearctic. The North American fauna may be analyzed in terms both of source and of current affinities. The difference between the two analyses is striking.

Also involved is a distinction between groups *autochthonous* in North America and those *endemic*—that is, now occurring nowhere else. There is no necessary correspondence between being autochthons and endemics, because an autochthonous group may well have spread to other regions and an endemic group may well have come from another region where it is now extinct. *Odocoileus* is autochthonous but not endemic in North America, and *Lama* is endemic but not autochthonous (as to family, at least) in South America.

### faunal stratification

In the whole world there is no known example of a fauna that is of uniform antiquity in the region occupied. (Quibbling exceptions could be made for a few volcanic islands that have been swept clean of life and repeopled in a rather short time, but that is of no real importance for the present point.) No fauna consists entirely of descendants of ancestors that entered the region together, but all are complexes of groups whose ancestors spread into the region at markedly different times. In that sense faunas can be said to be *stratified,* with older or younger strata of animals according to whether the animals' ancestors entered the region earlier or later.

The longer a group has been in a given region the more time there has been for evolution there, for divergence from ancestral types and local diversification and specialization. Thus it happens that as a rule with various exceptions the older strata of a regional fauna are more differentiated, more distinctive of that region, and less like the animals of other regions.

Although faunal stratification is virtually universal, it is not always clear-cut. Strata of different ages may be so numerous, as they are in North America, that they are difficult to disentangle. The island continents, Australia and South America, happen to have had relatively few and widely spaced invasions of mammals, with the result that their faunal strata are correspondingly few and are rather readily distinguishable. The example of South America, most fully documented, has been treated in sufficient detail elsewhere (Part 6 of this book). Analysis of faunal strata in Australia requires more inference because the known fossil record is relatively very poor there, but the mammalian fauna can nevertheless be divided into four strata with reasonable assurance, as shown here:

STRATIFICATION OF THE AUSTRALIAN MAMMALIAN FAUNA

| *Inferred Time of Emplacement* | *Faunal Stratum* | *Groups Included* | *Differentiation in Australia* |
|---|---|---|---|
| Late Pleistocene to Recent | IV Late Island-Hoppers | Rabbits and other historical introductions. Dingo. | None |
| Miocene | III Middle Island-Hoppers | Old World Rats | Numerous autochthonous genera, some subfamilies, no families or higher categories |
| Late Cretaceous or Early Tertiary | II Old Island-Hoppers | Marsupials | Great diversification and differentiation; numerous autochthonous families, some superfamilies or suborders. |
| Late Triassic or Jurassic | I Archaic Immigrants | Advanced mammal-like reptiles or early monotremes (pseudomammals?) | Platypus and echidnas, now fundamentally unlike any mammals of the rest of the world—a distinct subclass (at least). |

**basic continental faunal types**

Some of the fundamental differences among regional mammalian faunas reflect the fact that the Cenozoic mammalian faunas of different continents somehow got started from different stocks and in different ways. It is true that there was little really basic difference over much of the land area of the earth. Africa, the whole of Eurasia, and North America were early and repeatedly connected with each other by corridors and bridges. Many local faunal differences have occurred and still do, but in broader view the mammalian faunas of those continents are similar. They may be said to depart from and to represent a single World Continent basic faunal type. Each of the island continents, however, developed faunas that were, right from the beginning or soon thereafter, basically distinctive. Analysis requires inference and even some speculation, because the most pertinent faunas, those of the late Cretaceous and early Paleocene, are very poorly known. (Late Cretaceous mammals are known only from restricted areas in Asia and North America; early Paleocene mammals only from a small part of North America.) However, reasonable speculation labeled as such also has a legitimate place in science and can be interesting.

First, what world mammalian stocks were available as a source of continental faunas around the beginning of the Paleocene? There were some other groups, but three may be picked as key groups for the distinction of basic faunal types: marsupials, insectivores, and ferungulates. The original stock of the pouched mammals, the marsupials, consisted of small, obscure, more or less omnivorous, mainly arboreal, opossumlike creatures. Both insectivores and ferungulates were non-pouched: they were placental mammals. The early insectivores, potentially highly diverse, were small animals rather like the primitive marsupials in adaptive characteristics. The primitive ferungulates, potentially even more diverse, were larger, terrestrial, ambling or running animals, omnivorous at first but with a tendency to specialize either on fairly large animal food or on leaves or other vegetation.

Among the many different roles that mammals can play in a fauna, three broad adaptive types may also be picked out just for purposes of simplifying analysis: the insectivorous type, small creatures eating not only insects but also almost any small animal food, such as worms; the predaceous-carnivorous type, mostly medium-

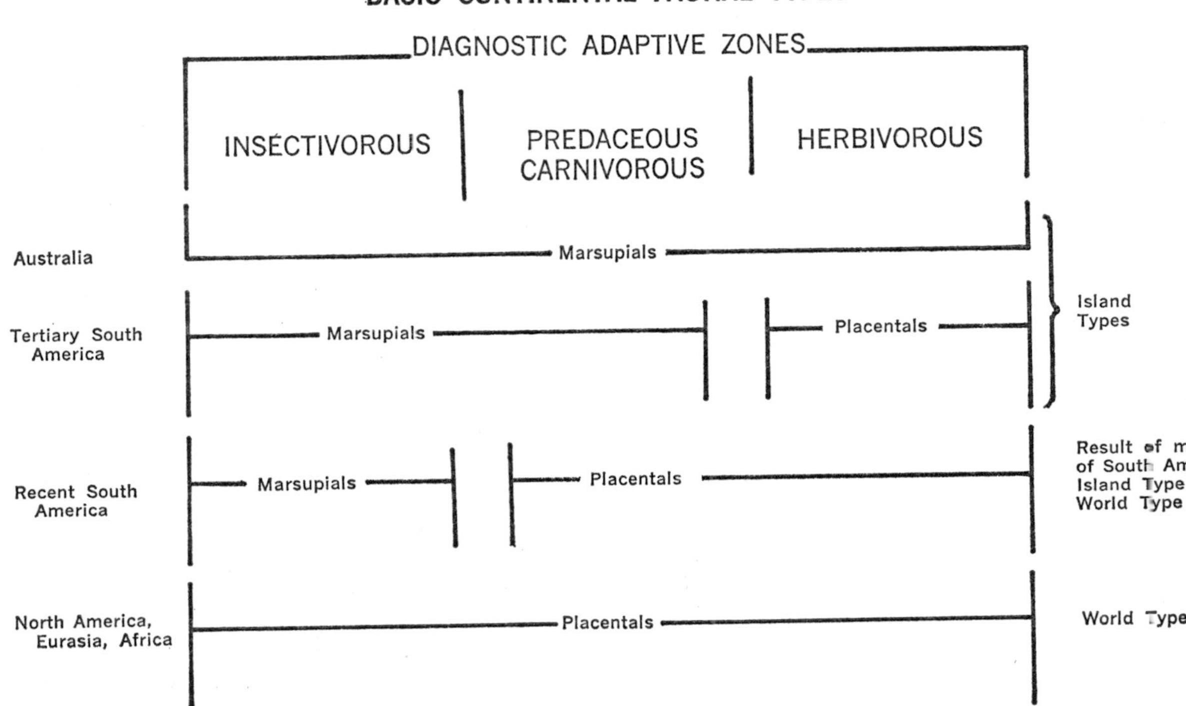
BASIC CONTINENTAL FAUNAL TYPES
DIAGNOSTIC ADAPTIVE ZONES
INSECTIVOROUS
PREDACEOUS CARNIVOROUS
HERBIVOROUS
Australia
Marsupials
Tertiary South America
Marsupials
Placentals
Island Types
Recent South America
Marsupials
Placentals
Result of mixture of South American Island Type and World Type
North America, Eurasia, Africa
Placentals
World Type

sized to large mammals killing and eating other animals, especially other mammals, up to their own size or even larger; and the herbivorous type, also medium-sized to very large, eating vegetation. In the basic World Continent fauna, all three of those adaptive types developed mainly or solely from placental mammals, the insectivorous type from (placental) insectivores and both the carnivorous and the herbivorous types from ferungulates. In Australia, however, all three adaptive types developed from marsupials. In South America the insectivorous and carnivorous types developed from marsupials, but the herbivorous type from placentals (ferungulates).

The classical theory as to why the basic Australian fauna developed almost entirely from marsupials was as follows: marsupials evolved before placentals; Australia was connected by land to the World Continent when only marsupials occurred there; later, when placentals had appeared on the World Continent, Australia had become an island and the placentals had no way of spreading to there. Although still occasionally supported, that theory is almost certainly wrong. There is no good evidence that marsupials did evolve before placentals. Both are present in the Cretaceous. They probably represent contemporaneously diverging lines of early mammalian evolution and not successive stages in the rise of higher mammals. If that is correct, we must suppose either that both placentals and marsupials entered Australia but only marsupials survived there, or that somehow only marsupials entered even though placentals existed and might have entered also. The former alternative is less probable. Marsupials can survive perfectly well in their own niches in a predominantly placental fauna, but nowhere are marsupials known to have completely replaced placentals living in the same faunas. If the second alternative is correct, it is almost incredible that Australia was connected to any part of the World Continent by a land bridge when the marsupials entered. Surely placentals would have used the bridge too. If, however, spread to Australia was by a sweepstakes route, entrance of marsupials, only, becomes credible and natural. Chances were against either group, and the marsupials just happened to get there

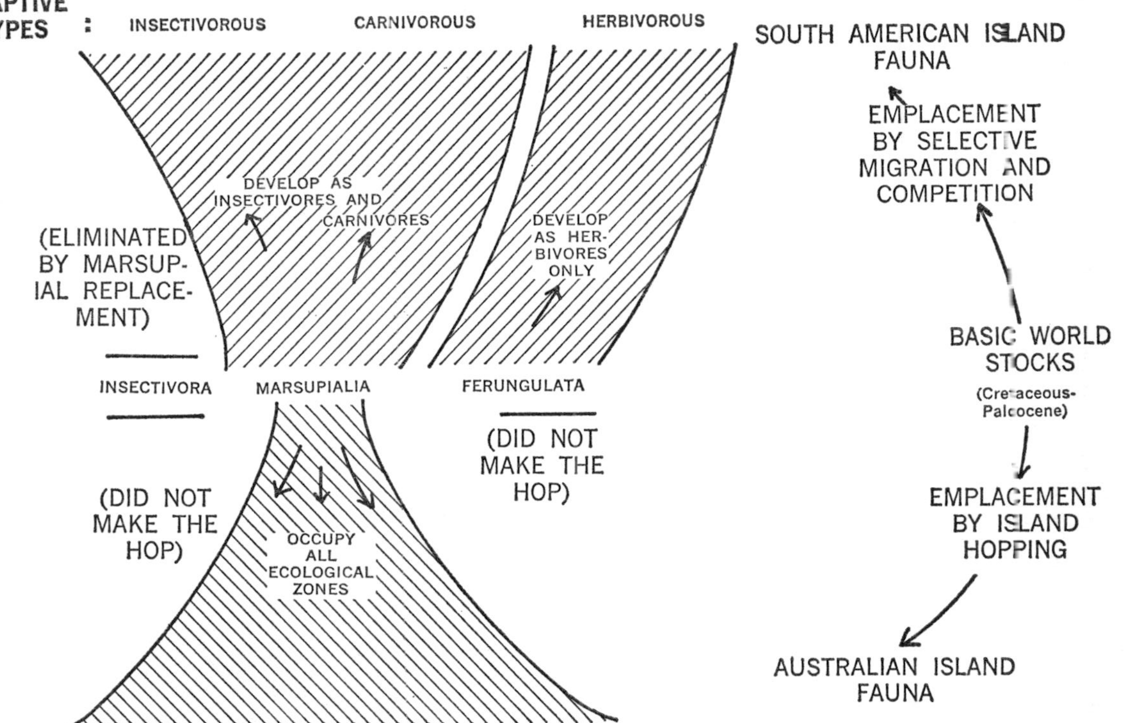


Fig. 20. Development of the mammalian faunas of the island continents (South America and Australia) from the basic world stocks.

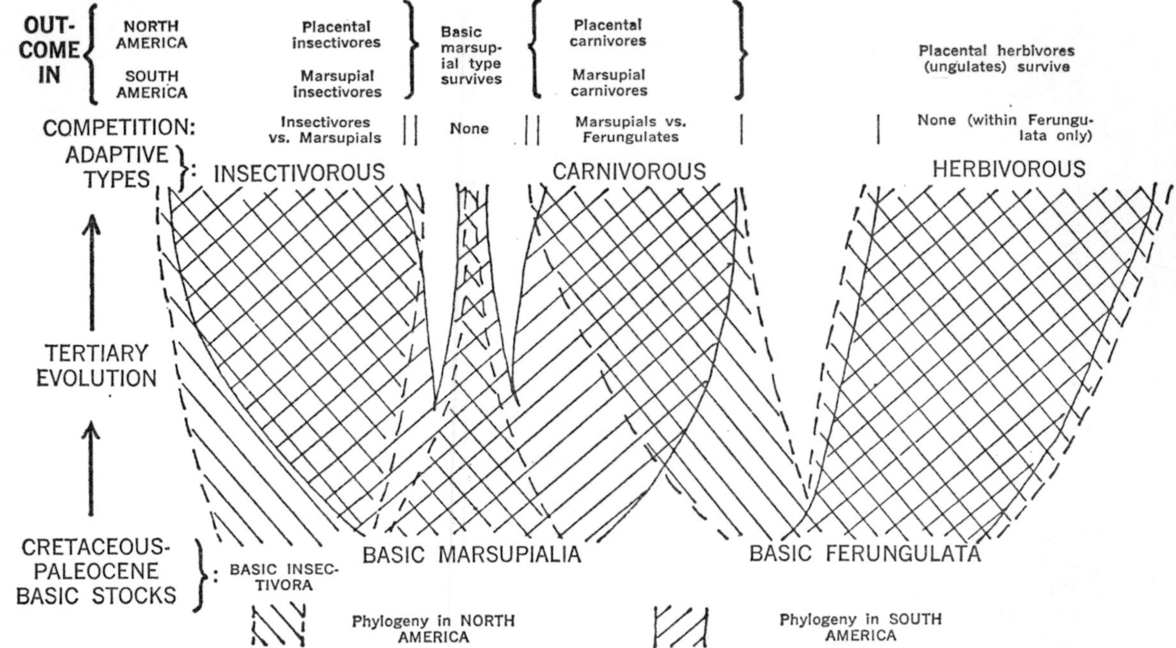


Fig: 21. Contrasting evolution of certain basic mammalian stocks in North and South America.

first (Fig. 20). The probability of this theory is enhanced by the fact that placentals (members of the rat family) are known to have reached Australia later and to have done so by a sweepstakes route, island-hopping from Asia. (Bats did so too; see Part 5.)

The basic peculiarity of the ancient South American faunas cannot be explained in the same way as for Australia. We know that diverse World Continent stocks early reached South America, including both marsupials and a variety of ferungulates. It seems probable that there was a land connection, almost surely with North America, and that the whole basic World Continent fauna did have access to South America just before it became an island continent. If that is correct, then marsupial evolution there must somehow have gotten a jump on that of some placentals. Marsupials may rapidly have replaced early insectivores in South America. It is still more probable that marsupials so early evolved predaceous carnivorous groups that the ferungulates did not evolve into those already occupied adaptive roles but only into herbivorous roles.

## 4. THE NORTH AMERICAN MAMMALIAN FAUNA

### taxonomic composition

The richness and general nature of the present North American fauna of land mammals is shown in the table below. (For an excellent, modern summary of the fauna, see Burt, 1952.) The sequence of earlier faunas throughout the Cenozoic is better known for this than for any other continent. The broadest feature is great increase in fundamental diversity, the number of major groups or orders, through the Paleocene and into the Eocene. After the early Eocene the number declined markedly into the middle Oligocene. Since the middle Oligocene the orders present have not always been the same, but their number has remained nearly constant (Fig. 22). There have been continuous, striking changes in composition of the fauna through the Cenozoic, as shown in Fig. 23.

SYNOPSIS OF RECENT NEARCTIC LAND ANIMALS *

| *Orders and families* | *No. of genera* | *No. of species* |
|---|---|---|
| MARSUPIALIA | 1 | 1 |
| Didelphidae, opossums | 1 | 1 |
| INSECTIVORA | 10 | 36 |
| Soricidae, shrews | 5 | 29 |
| Talpidae, moles | 5 | 7 |
| EDENTATA | 1 | 1 |
| Dasypodidae, armadillos | 1 | 1 |
| LAGOMORPHA | 3 | 14 |
| Ochotonidae, pikas | 1 | 1 |
| Leporidae, rabbits | 2 | 13 |
| RODENTIA | 35 | 165 |
| Aplodontidae, mountain beaver | 1 | 1 |
| Sciuridae, squirrels, etc. | 8 | 51 |
| Geomyidae, pocket gophers | 3 | 9 |
| RODENTIA (*cont'd*) | | |
| Heteromyidae, pocket mice and kangaroo rats | 3 | 36 |
| Castoridae, beavers | 1 | 1 |
| Cricetidae, native mice and rats | 16 | 63 |
| Zapodidae, jumping mice | 2 | 3 |
| Erethizontidae, porcupines | 1 | 1 |
| CARNIVORA | 16 | 30 |
| Canidae, wolves and foxes | 4 | 7 |
| Ursidae, bears | 1 | 4 |
| Procyonidae, raccoons, etc. | 2 | 2 |
| Mustelidae, weasels, skunks, etc. | 8 | 14 |
| Felidae, cats | 1 | 3 |
| ARTIODACTYLA | 5 | 6 |
| Antilocapridae, pronghorns | 1 | 1 |
| Bovidae, bison, sheep, goats | 4 | 5 |

TOTALS: Orders, 7; Familes, 21; Genera, 71; Species, 313.

* Orders are named in capitals and under each are listed the included families. Genera and species counted are non-aquatic native mammals, exclusive of bats, living in the United States and Canada. A few species that barely or occasionally cross the Mexican border but are of mainly Neotropical groups are omitted.

The most radical turnover, mostly by introduction of new groups and extinction of older ones, was during the Paleocene and Eocene (Fig. 24). A few early Paleocene orders were still present in the

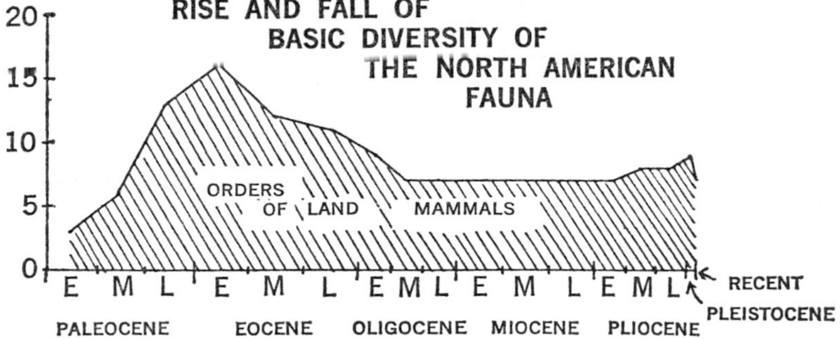


Fig. 22. Changes in fundamental diversity (number of orders) in the North American fauna. (Compare upper part of Fig. 14, which is a similar diagram for the whole world.)

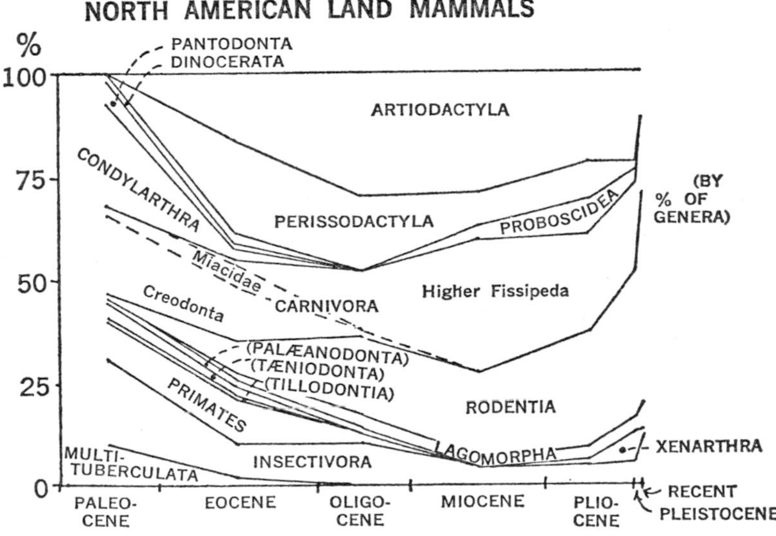


Fig. 23. Changes in known composition of the fauna of land mammals of North America through the Age of Mammals.

late Eocene, but those survivors constituted a decidedly minor part of the fauna except for the Order Carnivora. Even within that order the turnover was great, for most late Eocene carnivores were of quite different groups from their early Paleocene forerunners. Since the late Eocene there have been profound changes, to be sure, but these have been far less radical than the Paleocene-Eocene changes. As regards the broad orders, the most noteworthy changes since the late Eocene have been the extinction of the Perissodactyla (horses, rhinoceroses, tapirs, and their extinct relatives) and continuous great expansion of the rodents, which now constitute about half of the North American fauna (in terms of both genera and species).

The accompanying figures (23, 24) show changes in percentage composition. It is more difficult to estimate changes in absolute numbers of genera and species, because we do not know all those groups before the Recent, and it is impossible to be sure what proportion of them we do know for various times. The general impression is that the numbers of genera and species increased greatly and rather steadily from the early Paleocene onward perhaps into the Miocene. In the Pliocene and Pleistocene the numbers were still high but perhaps lower than in the Miocene, and since some time in the Pleistocene they have almost certainly decreased.

### age composition

Several North American families (Aplodontidae, Geomyidae, Heteromyidae, and Antilocapridae), many genera, and most species are endemic. On the other hand, most of the families also occur on other continents, and so do more than half of the genera a number of species. (For example, our wolf, *Canis lupus,* is not specifically separable from that of Eurasia, nor is our puma, *Felis concolor,* from that of South America.) Other factors are also involved, but these varying degrees of distinctivenes of members of our fauna are in part a reflection of the fact that the fauna is complexly stratified. The complexity is, indeed, so great that all the separate strata have not yet been clearly recognized or their mem-

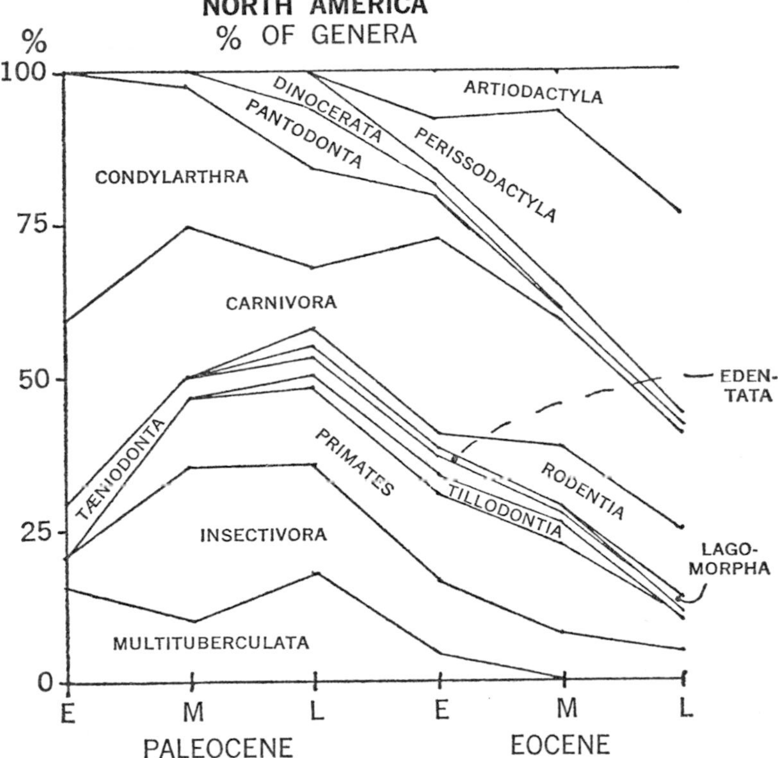


Fig. 24. Changing composition of the North America fauna of land mammals during the first two epochs of the Age of Mammals. This shows in greater detail the first part of the history seen in Fig. 23. The most striking fact is the radical turnover in basic composition, with most of the early groups largely or wholly replaced by later groups.

bers sorted out. It is, nevertheless, possible to make an approximation of broad stratal analysis by determining the ages of the various families of mammals present now and through the Cenozoic.

Fig. 25 presents data for first appearance and survival of known families of land mammals from late Cretaceous onward and for the whole world. Offhand one might expect that first appearances would decrease and survival would increase as time went on. There is perhaps some such tendency, but it is not strong or regular. First appearances were highest in the Eocene and survival is greatest from the Oligocene. Fig. 26 presents in different graphic style a similar analysis for appearance and survival in North America, only. Effects of the great Paleocene-Eocene turnover (Fig. 24) are evident: in North America no Paleocene family survived later than the Miocene. As for the world as a whole, in North America more families of Oligocene first appearance still survive than for any other epoch. The stratal complexity is reflected by the fact that the families of mammals now living in North America first appeared here at various times from the late Cretaceous (some 80 million years or more ago) onward.

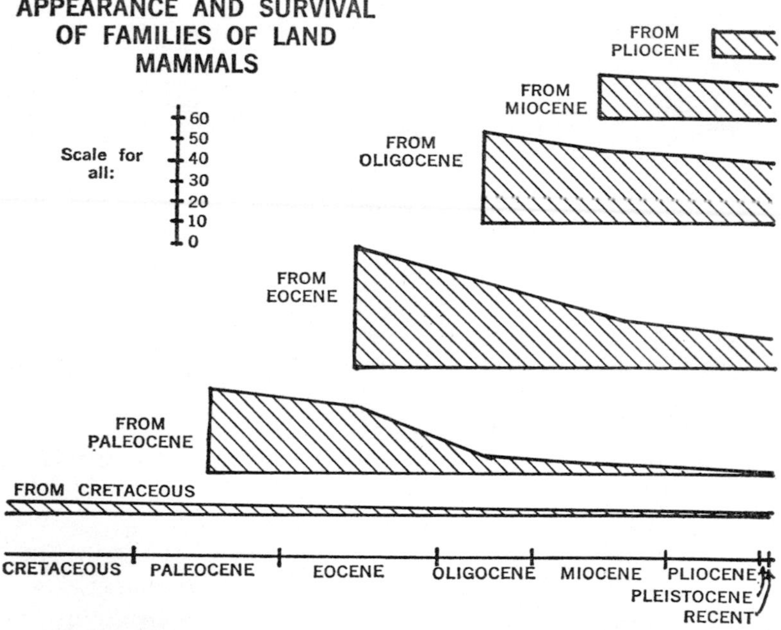


Fig. 25. Appearance and survival of families of land mammals for the world as a whole.

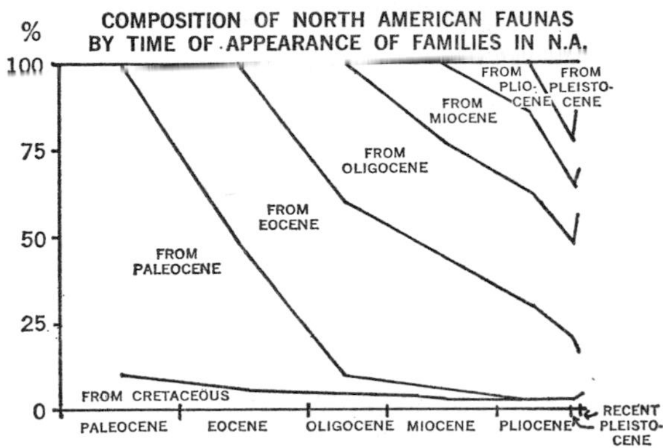


Fig. 26. The changing composition of the North American families of land mammals in terms of the age of the families from their first appearances in North America.

### faunal interchange and sources

When a new group of land mammals, say a family or a genus, appeared in North America it came from one or another of the following sources:

North America, itself, by evolutionary change from an older group.
South America
Asia
Europe

Other possibilities, perhaps such as spread from the West Indies, Africa, or the Southwest Pacific, perhaps cannot wholly be ruled out, but they are highly improbable and there seems to be no evidence at all that any North American land animals ever did come directly from any geographic source other than the four just named. In fact the evidence that any mammals, at least, came directly from Europe is poor, and there is some probability that North American faunal interchanges have involved only South America and Asia (or Eurasia through Asia).

The occurrence of truly related animals in both of two regions is conclusive evidence that there has been some degree of faunal interchange between the regions at some time in the past. It does not necessarily indicate a direct interchange. For example tapirs now occur only in the Oriental and Neotropical Regions, but there has certainly never been faunal interchange directly between those two regions. The distribution of tapirs is the result of interchanges between Oriental and Palaearctic, Palaearctic and Nearctic, and Nearctic and Neotropical Regions, as their occurrence as fossils in the Palaearctic and Nearctic plainly demonstrates.

As a rule, the more closely related are animals in two different regions the more direct and more recent was a faunal interchange between those regions. In attempting this sort of analysis between the faunas of different continents it is usually of little practical use to seek extremely closely related groups, those classified as belonging to the same species. The processes of spread from one continent to another and of early adjustment to conditions on a different continent are usually accompanied by evolutionary changes that cause the animals to be considered different species. Almost always, however, they are still recognizable as belonging to the same genus. It is, then, a justified postulate of study of continental faunal interchanges that the occurrence of the same genus on two different continents indicates spread from one to the other and places that spread as having occurred not long before, geologically speaking. "Not long before" is a vague expression and the time doubtless varies greatly, possibly up to several million years, but it is likely

Fig. 27. A characteristic item of evidence for faunal interchange between two continents. The drawings are of upper teeth of small, weasel-like extinct animals. Although different in detail they are similar and are placed in one genus: *Palaeogale,* Specimen (a) is from Mongolia and (b) from Colorado.

to be short in proportion to the 75 million years, more or less, of the Age of Mammals.

Each occurrence of related animals on two continents is an item of evidence for intermigration between them (Fig. 27). By study of faunas at successive times during the Cenozoic, such items can be added together for each definable time span. A picture is then obtained of increase and decrease in migration intensity. Between North and South America the sequence is rather simple. After the Paleocene, at least, there was no real interchange until well along in the Miocene. Some time before that, late Eocene to late Oligocene, two groups of North American mammals probably did reach South America (a group of rodents and one of primates), but they probably did so by island-hopping across a central American sweepstakes route. In the late Miocene some North American

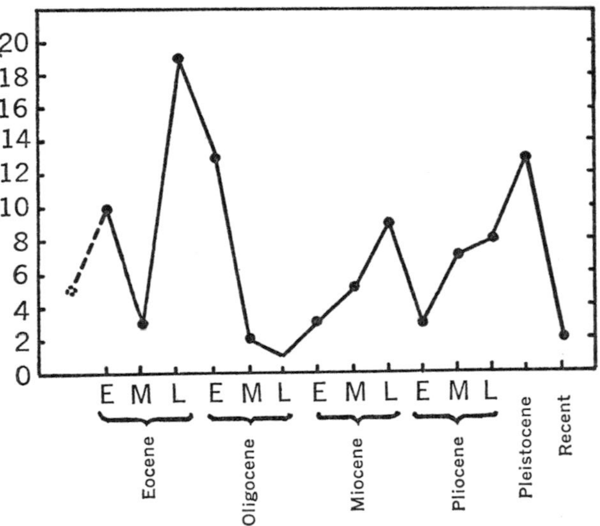


Fig. 28. Numbers of items of evidence for interchange of land mammals between Eurasia and North America through most of the Age of Mammals. The intensity of actual interchange doubtless rather closely followed the ups and downs shown here.

members of the raccoon family reached South America and some South American ground sloths reached North America. They probably also island-hopped. From late Pliocene into the Pleistocene occurred the intense intermigration discussed on a previous page. This enriched the North American Pleistocene fauna and gave it a bizarre aspect by introducing more ground sloths, glyptodonts, large armadillos, and capybaras (giant rodents related to the guinea pig). The influence is not very evident now, for only two mammals of South American origin, our armadillo and our porcupine, remain well-established in the Nearctic Region.

Faunal interchange between Eurasia and North America has been more frequent and more intense. Some of the items of evidence are summed up in the graph of Fig. 28. Times of exceptionally intense intermigration included early Eocene, early Oligocene, late Miocene, and Pleistocene. Middle (perhaps also early) Miocene, and middle and late Pliocene were times of less but still significant intermigration. In the middle Eocene, middle and late Oligocene, and early Pliocene there were times of little or no intermigration, and this is true also of the Recent, when we know that strong barriers exist. (There are, to be sure, some items of evidence for intermigration at the stated times, but these evidently reflect either slightly earlier migrations or the fact that interruption may not have continued through the whole time span in question.)

Such evidence permits further inferences. When interchange was moderate to high, there certainly was a land route between Eurasia and North America, because considerable essentially simultaneous spread in both directions can hardly be accounted for by a sweepstakes route. It further follows that the land connection was probably interrupted by a sea barrier when interchange was slight or nil, although this negative inference is less certain than the positive inference of presence of a land bridge at other times. Even the most intense interchanges involved only a fraction of the whole faunas of the continents. It may therefore be concluded that the connection was a filter bridge rather than a corridor. Study of what kinds of mammals were passed or stopped by the filter suggests (although the evidence is not yet completely conclusive) that those stopped were the ones adapted exclusively to tropical climates or, at least, not at home in the cooler climates of each epoch. Studies of resemblances between North American faunas and those of different parts of Eurasia, a point to which I will return, further demonstrate that during and after the late Eocene, at least, resemblance is closest with faunas of northeastern Asia. All this and other evidence supports the conclusion that the filter bridge was in the north and that it connected Asia and North America more or less in the regions now designated as eastern Siberia and Alaska. The possibility of an early Cenozoic land connection also with Europe is not conclusively ruled out, but such a connection is not necessary to explain any known facts and it is improbable in the light of present knowledge.

(The Eurasian-North American faunal interchange is discussed in much greater detail in Simpson, 1947 a, b.)

## 5. FAUNAL RESEMBLANCES

### problems of evidence and interpretation

The historical approach to biogeography gives new meaning to the study of faunal resemblances with which the 19th-century biogeographers and many of their successors were mainly concerned. New light is cast on faunal resemblances and some major problems have been solved by considering the different patterns of geographic distribution as they change through time. A comparatively simple pattern is origin of a group on one continent and spread to others. For example, the family Bovidae (cattle, sheep, antelopes, etc.) arose in Eurasia, probably in southern Asia, and expanded its area of distribution until it now occurs on all continents except Australia and South America. Another pattern shows expansion followed by contraction. Mastodonts arose in the Old World, probably in Africa, spread to all continents except Australia, then contracted and became extinct. The elephants, a progressive offshoot from the mastodonts, spread to all continents except Australia and South America (exceptions to so many zoogeographical generalizations) and now survive only in part of the Oriental and Ethiopian Regions.

Further complexities arise when groups become extinct in their homelands. Evolution of the horse and camel families was long centered in North America, whence they spread very widely at various times, but neither family has native survivors in North America. Still another common pattern is early spread of a primitive group to two or more regions and then separate evolution of its descendants in each region. The true pigs and the peccaries, the so-called wild pigs of South America and southern North America, are an example. The group originated in the Old World, whence one line spread to North America and here evolved in parallel with but henceforth quite separately from the Old World pigs. Then there are groups that have throughout their whole known histories remained in one region or continent and that therefore are the most truly distinctive of zoogeographic markers. Through most of the Cenozoic (late Eocene to middle Pliocene) North America swarmed with the extinct artiodactyls called oreodonts, but none spread to any other continent. Our unique pronghorns or so-called antelopes are not true antelopes but belong to a native North American group (the family Antilocapridae), once much more numerous and diverse than now but never spread to any other region. Giraffes moved about in Eurasia and Africa but they never reached the New World. There are many other such groups, always confined to one region or another, although most major groups of mammals (families, at least) on the "World Continent" continents of Africa, Eurasia, and North America did at one time or another spread over two or more of those continents. The island continents of course developed a high proportion of families and other groups unique to them.

One of the classical problems of biogeography is that of disjunctive distributions—that is, the occurrence of similar plants or animals in widely separated areas and the absence of equally similar forms in intervening areas. Such similarities demonstrate spread or migration between the two regions, but they pose problems as to whether the route followed was more or less direct and whether spread was of more or less remotely ancestral forms. A classical example is the recent occurrence of tapirs in the Neotropical and Oriental Regions, already mentioned and explained as due to spread through the Palaearctic and Nearctic Regions.

The problems of evaluating such similarities and inferring their historical origins is often one of determining the degree and nature of the real relationship between the similar forms in two regions. Examples that have given rise to much discussion concern the South American fauna. As previously noted, predaceous marsupial carnivores have occurred in Australia and South America, and they are unknown from any other parts of the world. If those groups were really closely related in the two continents, spread between the two must have occurred after the predaceous marsupials had become specialized as such. In that case, it would be probable, at least, that the route was not through northern continents but was a South Pacific continent or a land bridge connection through Antarctica (where no fossil mammals are known). Biogeographers long assumed that such was the history. It is now clear, however, that the two groups are not closely related but are examples of convergence in the parallel radiations of the two island continents. Predaceous types developed independently in both continents from early, primitive, non-predaceous, opossum-like ancestors such as are known in both North America and Eurasia. (See Simpson, 1948.)

A still greater puzzle has been the distribution of the porcupines and some of their allies. The North American porcupine is a relatively late immigrant from South America. The native South American porcupines and some other native rodents there resemble the porcupines and some other rodents of Africa. If this resemblance resulted from geographic spread after porcupines and other specialized rodents had evolved, it would be almost necessary to conclude that migration was at a rather late date and that the route was across what is now the South Atlantic. The question, then, could be put thus in oversimplified terms: "Are South American and African porcupines brothers?" The answer, provided mainly by early fossil rodents, seems to be "No." This turns out

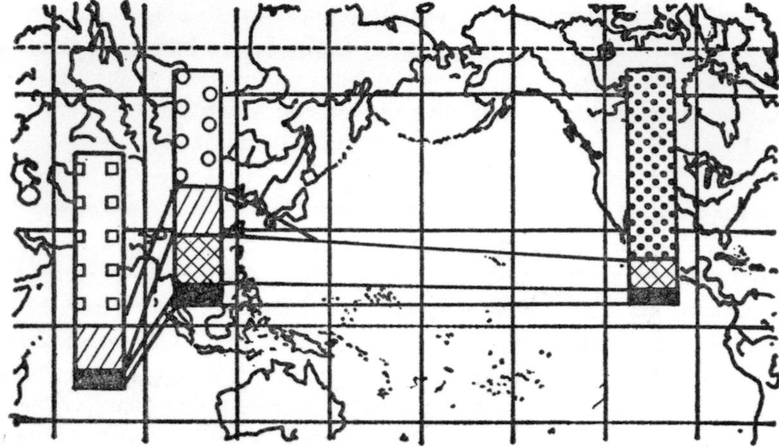

Fig. 29. Resemblances among three ancient faunas of land mammals. The faunas are those known from India, Mongolia, and the United States in the latest Miocene or earliest Pliocene. The upper parts of the bars, with different patterns, represent in each case the percentage of genera confined to that region as among these three. The other patterns show percentages common to two or (black) to all three. Note that the Mongolian fauna is at least as similar to the North American as to the Indian, although it is much closer to India.

to be another example of convergence in separate parallel radiations. The ancestors of the New World porcupines were unspecialized early North American rodents (see Wood, 1950).

## measurement and examples of faunal resemblance

Different groups in a single fauna may have had quite different geographical histories. The porcupines of our coniferous forests are from a geographic source entirely different from that of any other mammal in those forests. The history of each group must be considered on its own merits, but it can be correctly interpreted only in the light of general faunal interchanges and of total faunal resemblances. Significant resemblances are those reflecting actual blood (phylogenetic) relationships of the various animals in the faunas being compared. The degree of such relationships is roughly and somewhat subjectively but still usefully designated by the classification of the animals concerned: those placed in the same species are very closely related; those placed in different species but the same genus are less closely related; those referred to different genera but the same family are still more distantly related; members of different families but of the same order represent a definite but comparatively quite distant relationship.

As would be expected, the broader the group or the higher the category of classification used in comparison, the higher the percentage of groups common to two regions, as exemplified in the table below. (See also Simpson, 1936.) Comparisons must be

NUMBERS OF ORDERS, FAMILIES, GENERA, AND SPECIES OF LAND MAMMALS IN OREGON AND NEW YORK STATES AND THOSE COMMON TO BOTH

| | *Oregon* | *New York* | *Both* | *100 C/N₁** |
|---|---|---|---|---|
| Orders | 5 | 6 | 5 | 100 |
| Families | 19 | 15 | 14 | 93 |
| Genera | 45 | 37 | 25 | 68 |
| Species | 93 | 50 | 23 | 46 |

* 100 $C/N_1$ is the percentage of members of the smaller fauna also present in the larger fauna.

based on an explicit category, species, genus, or other, and interpreted in the light of the particular degree of relationship involved. The actual measurement of faunal resemblance may be made in various ways, three of which will be exemplified. In Fig. 20 comparison is simply by the percentage of genera in each fauna unique to it or shared with one or both of the other two faunas. The example incidentally shows that at the stated time the northeastern Asiatic fauna resembled the southern Asiatic and the North American faunas about equally but that the latter two faunas had very little resemblance to each other. That is part of the evidence for the conclusion, previously stated, that faunal interchange between Asia and North America was by a northern route.

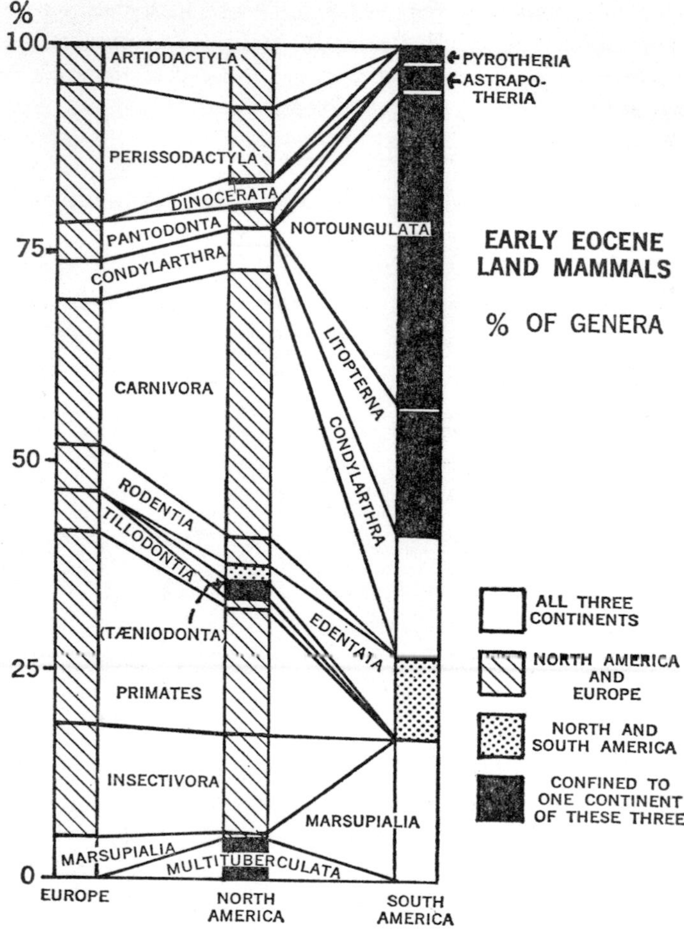


Fig. 30. Comparison of three ancient faunas of land mammals. Each bar represents the known early Eocene fauna of a continent, the composition shown by percentage of genera belonging to each order. The shading indicates the distribution of the orders on the three continents. Similarity of European and North America faunas and radical dissimilarity of the South American fauna are evident.

Fig. 30 makes broader comparisons by different measurements: the percentages of genera in each fauna belonging to orders unique to the fauna or shared with one or two others. The example clearly brings out the fact that in the early Eocene the European and North American faunas had most of their orders in common and were also rather similar in percentage composition. The South American fauna, on the other hand, was radically unlike either of the others. These resemblances and differences are of course evidence of the spread through Eurasia and North America of the basic World Continent faunal type and of active early Eocene interchange between them, while South America was an island continent with its own basic faunal type.

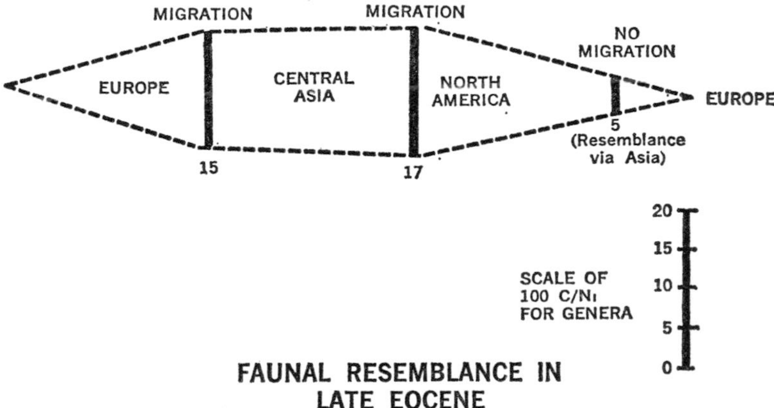


Fig. 31. Resemblances of known late Eocene faunas of land mammals in Europe, Central Asia, and North America. The vertical lines indicate resemblances, measured as explained in the text, between the regions named.

In Fig. 31 comparison is by an index of faunal resemblance which is particularly useful in historical and other biogeographic studies. The index is symbolized as 100 $C/N_1$, in which C stands for the number of taxonomic units (genera in this example) common to the two faunas and $N_1$ is the total number of units in the smaller of the two. (The reasons for using this particular index and some of its special characteristics are discussed in Simpson, 1943 a, 1947 a.) The data of the example show that the late Eocene mammals of Central Asia about equally resemble those of Europe and North America. There was some interchange in both directions, probably through a filter in each case. On the other hand, the resemblance between North America and Europe is much lower and is consistent with the conclusion that those regions were connected through Asia and not directly with each other. (That conclusion is further supported by the fact that the few genera common to Europe and North America also occurred in Asia.)

Like all other characteristics of faunas, their resemblances de-

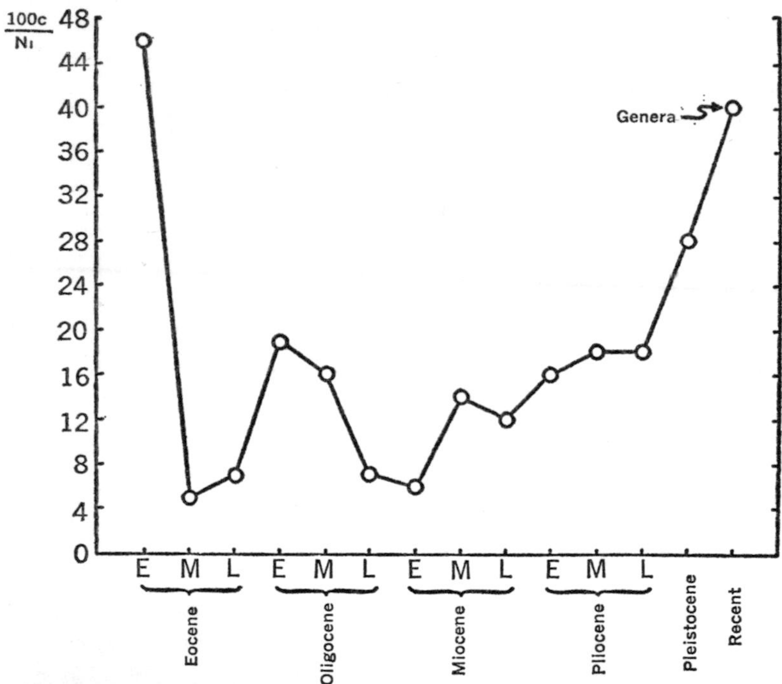


Fig. 32. Fluctuating resemblances of known faunas of land mammals between Eurasia and North America through most of the Age of Mammals.

velop historically and change through time. Fig. 32 shows the generic resemblances of the North American mammalian fauna from early Eocene to Recent.

### factors influencing faunal resemblances

When faunal interchange occurs between two areas, resemblance between their faunas tends to increase. That is obvious, and it is one of the essential factors in the existence of faunal resemblances and in changes of such resemblances. It is, however, far from being the only factor and in particular instances it may not be the most important factor. If changes in faunal resemblance between North America and Eurasia (Fig. 32) are compared with changes in intensity of faunal interchange (Fig. 28), the two curves evidently have some relationship to each other but they are far from running parallel. Faunal resemblance may be low, as it was in the late Eocene, when interchange was high, and may be high, as it is now, when interchange is low. There is a tendency for greater faunal resemblance to occur after rather than during intense interchange, but even this tendency is highly irregular.

One important factor, stressed previously in this essay, is ecological. The faunas of similar environments are more similar than are those of different environments, regardless of differences in geographic position. That is a matter of common observation familiar to anyone who has noticed the animals of diverse environments. It must be taken into account in interpreting the resemblances of any faunas, fossil or recent. For instance, fossils from the Tiffany beds of southwestern Colorado represent mammals all of which lived in an area of a few square miles and at about the same time (in the late Paleocene). Some were found scattered in the beds ("surface finds") and some in a single small pocket ("Mason pocket"). The two lots are samples of animals that lived in different ecological associations. Their resemblance in terms of $100\ C/N_1$ for genera is only 20. But the index of resemblance of the "surface" fauna to another "surface" fauna (Paskapoo) in distant Alberta, Canada, is 60, and the index between the "pocket" fauna and an ecologically similar collection (Scarritt Quarry) in Montana is 50. Thus each of these faunas resembles an ecologically similar fauna in a distant area much more than it does an ecologically distinct fauna in the same area.

Comparison of large regions each with a variety of environments does not wholly eliminate ecological differences, but in such cases other factors usually outweigh the purely ecological. That is particularly true of comparisons of fauna of whole continents, on each of which many broad sorts of environments are duplicated. The index 100 $C/N_1$ also tends to minimize merely ecological differences, because its value is little affected if one fauna happens to differ from another in occupying a region of more diverse environments.

Another factor affecting faunal resemblances is distance. Even though ecological conditions are similar and there is no filter or barrier between them, faunas tend to be less similar the more distant they are from each other. This is exemplified in the table below. Comparison of A with the additional data of B strongly suggests that there have never been Cenozoic connections directly between North America and Europe or South America and Africa, a point to be discussed next.

FAUNAL RESEMBLANCES MEASURED BY 100 $C/N_1$ FOR GENERA OF LAND MAMMALS

| | 100 $C/N_1$ |
|---|---|
| A. For Recent faunas on parts of a continuous land mass | |
| Distance 500 miles (Ohio–Nebraska) | 82 |
| Distance 1,000 miles (Florida–New Mexico) | 67 |
| Distance 5,000 miles (France–China) | 64 |
| B. For ancient faunas | |
| Western U.S.A.–Western Europe in early Eocene | 45 |
| (This is the closest resemblance known between any Old World and New World land faunas. The distance is about 5,000 miles via the North Atlantic and about 10,000 miles via the North Pacific and Asia.) | |
| South America–Africa, all know faunas | 0 |

The effect of filters and barriers is of course that they limit or prevent faunal interchange. Resemblances may, however, increase or decrease regardless of whether faunal interchange is occurring between the regions being compared. The endemics of a region make its fauna different from those of other regions. Their extinction therefore increases faunal resemblances by decreasing dissimilarities. Other factors decrease resemblance. In any region the animals are likely to undergo local evolutionary differentiation and progressive change and hence to become less like their relatives in other regions—that is a universal phenomenon which underlies the (negative) correlation of faunal resemblance with distance. Or, after a group has expanded from one region to another, increasing faunal resemblance between them, it may become extinct in one but not the other, decreasing the resemblance. That is true, for instance, of the camels. In the Pliocene the presence of camels in North but not South America was a faunal dissimilarity. In the Pleistocene their presence in both regions was a similarity. Now their presence in South but not North America is given as one of the definitive differences between Neotropical and Nearctic Regions. (The example incidentally shows that definitions of such regions based on their present faunas may become invalid or extremely confusing when the history of the faunas is taken into account.)

All those and still other factors interact constantly as faunas change through time. Faunal resemblances and their changes are the resultants of intricate complexes of evolutionary and geographic events. (This topic, too, is more fully treated in Simpson, 1947 a.)

## 6. FAUNAL HISTORY AND EARTH HISTORY

### schools of paleogeographic theory

It has long been known that the geography of the earth has changed greatly during the course of its history. Seas often occurred where now is land. Continents have changed in shape and in their connections with each other. Paleogeography, the historical approach to physical geography, has as its aim the reconstruction of all such geographical events. It also has deeper implications, for it involves an understanding of the whole construction of the earth and especially of the nature and mechanics of the crust of the earth. Here historical biogeography has a crucial part to play. The sequences and relationships of past faunas are always pertinent evidence and sometimes the only good evidence of ancient geographical conditions. Hence not only must paleogeography be used as framework for biogeography, but also biogeography must be used as a criterion for theories of paleogeography.

Some earlier paleogeographers postulated that land and sea segments of the earth's crust differ in no really essential way. Which is land and which sea was supposed to depend not on local characteristics of the crust itself but simply on whether segments happened to be uplifted or not. Theorists of that school envisioned the presence of vast continents where now are the Pacific, Atlantic, and Indian Oceans. Earlier geographical developments of faunas were supposed to have occurred on a map unrecognizably different from that of today. Such extreme views no longer have any informed supporters. Land and sea segments of the crust are known to be different in average composition. Practically everyone now agrees that during most of the history of life there has been some degree of constancy or continuous identity in the continental and oceanic segments of the earth's crust, despite great changes in outline and other details.

That conclusion still leaves room for disagreement as to the nature and position of past connections between continental blocks. One school of theory has indulged in the extravagant postulation of land bridges between the continents. No two students of that school have agreed precisely as to when or where the bridges existed, but their maps show the oceans crisscrossed with isthmian connections, from Europe across the South Atlantic to South America and across the Indian Ocean to India, from Asia or Australia across the Pacific to America, from Australia and South America to Antarctica, and so on.

Another school, especially associated with the name of the German geologist Wegener although others before and after him have developed similar theories, holds that the continental segments have been floating blocks drifting on the deeper parts of the crust. The theory is that the continental segments once formed a single mass, or two of them, which then broke up into the present continents. The separation and present placing of the continents are supposed to have resulted from slow drifting apart of fragments of the original block or blocks.

Finally, there is a school which holds, with the land bridge builders, that continents and oceans have tended to maintain their identities and positions through most of geological history, but which minimizes the number of vanished connections between the continents. The former existence of any bridge over what is now an ocean is considered highly doubtful or rejected altogether. The past existence of a few bridges across what now are island arcs or straits is considered sufficient to account for all known biogeographical events.

### evidence from historical biogeography

The numerous different theories of paleogeography are susceptible to crucial testing by the facts of biogeography. If a South Atlantic bridge once arose between South America and Africa, the faunas of that time should attest the fact, just as the faunas of North and South America plainly show the rise of a bridge between them in the Pliocene. If South America and Africa were parts of a single continent, as both the transoceanic continent and the drifting continent schools have claimed for various times in the past, then the faunas of that time should be related more or less as the faunas of single continents today. As has been shown above, it is possible to measure faunal interchanges and resemblances. It is not necessary, as was so often done in the past, to argue vaguely "I think the faunas are so similar that they belonged to one continent," and counter with "I think they are not." The data that have been given should, for instance, end all argument that Africa and South America were connected to each other at any time during the Cenozoic, because in contrast with those figures the index of generic resemblance for all known Cenozoic faunas of the two continents is zero.

The pertinent evidence and conclusions have in large part already been summarized on previous pages. An instructive fur-

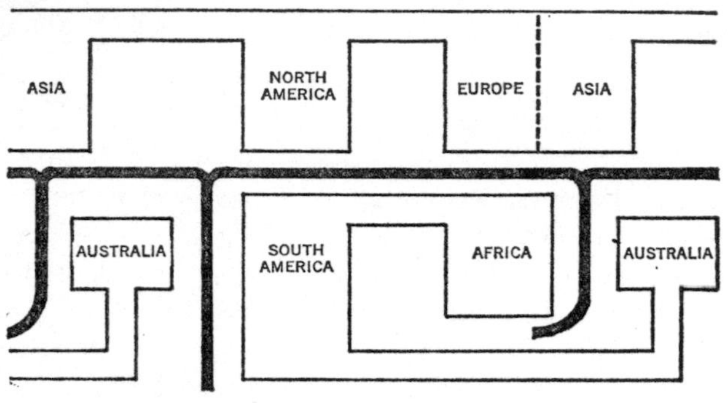


ACCORDING TO WEGENER

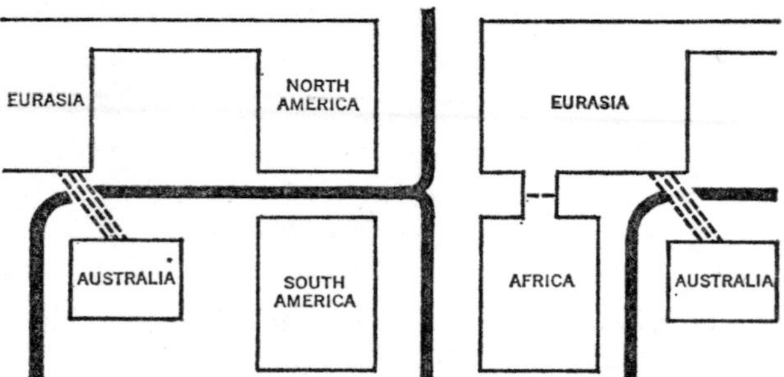


ACCORDING TO FOSSILS AND RELATED EVIDENCE

— EOCENE —

Fig. 33. A zoogeographical test of a paleogeographic theory. The upper figure shows the connections and barriers between continental blocks in the Eocene according to Wegener's version of the theory of drifting continents. The lower figure shows the connections and barriers demanded by known faunal resemblances and differences. Wegener's ideas of Eocene geography were evidently wrong.

ther step is to make diagrams of continental relationships according to the various theories and according to concretely measured faunal interchanges and resemblances. The precise outlines of the continents do not matter for this purpose, and even their positions on the surface of the globe may be ignored provided that supposed or inferred corridors, bridges, and sweepstakes routes are appropriately represented in the diagrams. Fig. 33 shows such diagrams for the Eocene according to one theory of continental drift (Wegener's) and according to the most probable interpretation of the biogeographic data. Radical discrepancy is obvious, and it is hardly possible that Wegener was right in his ideas of Eocene geography.

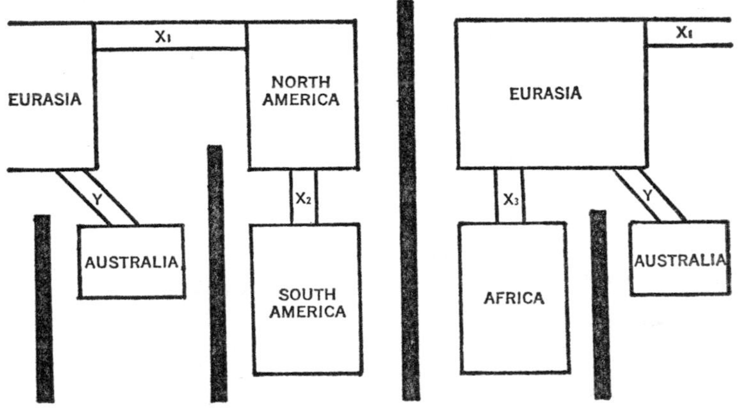


$X_{1,2,3}$ — THE VARIABLE MAJOR FILTER BRIDGES AND CORRIDORS

Y — A VARIABLE SWEEPSTAKES ROUTE

▌— CONSTANT BARRIERS DURING CENOZOIC

**THE CENOZOIC WORLD**

Fig. 34. The world of the Age of Mammals. Major features of the geographic history of mammals are best accounted for by considering the continental blocks and the main sea barriers as constants and three main filter bridges and one main sweepstakes route as variables.

All the biogeographic features in the known history of mammals are best accounted for on the theory that the continents have had their present identities and positions and that there have been no land bridges additional to those that now exist (North-South America and Eurasia-Africa) except for a northern Asia-North America bridge (Fig. 34). Additional features are largely matters of local detail. The connection between eastern and western Eurasia has not always been a corridor and may even have been briefly broken. The Eurasia-Africa bridge has varied in extent and in position, and other bridges have also varied in these respects. An Asia-Australia bridge may well have existed some time before the Cenozoic. There were probably early sweepstakes routes (but not complete bridges) from Antarctica to Australia and South America.

With such amplifications, the conclusion seems to apply not only to the biogeography of mammals but also to that of all contemporaneous forms of life. It remains possible that there were transoceanic continents or bridges, or that continents drifted in the Triassic or earlier, but there is little good evidence that such was the fact. In any case such remote events would have little or no bearing on the present distribution of living things.

(The bearings of biogeography on paleogeography are more fully discussed in Simpson, 1940 a, b; 1943 a; 1949 a.)

#### REFERENCES

ALLEE, W. C., A. E. EMERSON, O. PARK, T. PARK, AND K. P. SCHMIDT. 1949. *Principles of Animal Ecology*. Saunders, Philadelphia.

DE BEAUFORT, L. F. 1951. *Zoogeography of the Land and Inland Waters.* Sidgwick and Jackson, London.

BURT, W. H. 1952, *A Field Guide to the Mammals*. Houghton Mifflin, Boston.

DARLINGTON, P. J. 1957. *Zoogeography: The Geographic Distribution of Animals*. Wiley, New York.

HESSE, R., W. C. ALLEE, AND K. P. SCHMIDT. 1951. *Ecological Animal Geography,* 2nd ed. Wiley, New York.

LYDEKKER, R. 1896. *A Geographical History of Mammals*. Cambridge Univ. Press, Cambridge.

MATTHEW, W. D. 1915. Climate and Evolution. *Ann. New York Acad. Sci.*, **24**: 171–318. (Reprinted, 1939, with other relevant matter as vol. 1, Special Publications, New York Acad. Sci.)

MILLOT, J. 1952. La Faune Malgache et le Mythe Gondwanien. *Mém. Inst. Sci. Madagascar,* Sér. A, **7**: 1–36.

OSBORN, H. F. 1910. *The Age of Mammals.* Macmillan, New York.

SCLATER, W. L., AND P. L. SCLATER. 1899. *The Geography of Mammals.* Kegan, Paul, Trench, Trübner, London.

SIMPSON, G. G. 1936. Data on the Relationships of Local and Continental Mammalian Faunas. *Jour. Paleont.*, **10**: 410–414.

———. 1940 a. Mammals and Land Bridges. *Jour. Washington Acad. Sci.*, **30**: 137–163.

———. 1940 b. Antarctica as a Faunal Migration Route, *Proc. 6th Pacific Sci. Cong.:* 755–768.

———. 1943 a. Mammals and the Nature of Continents. *Amer. Jour. Sci.*, **241**: 1–31.

———. 1943 b. Turtles and the Origin of the Fauna of Latin America. *Amer. Jour. Sci.*, **241**: 413–429.

———. 1947 a. Holarctic Mammalian Faunas and Continental Relationships During the Cenozoic. *Bull. Geol. Soc. Amer.*, **58**: 613–688.

———. 1947 b. Evolution, Interchange, Resemblance of the North American and Eurasian Cenozoic Mammalian Faunas. *Evolution,* **1**: 218–220.

———. 1948. The Beginning of the Age of Mammals in South America. Part 1. *Bull. Amer. Mus. Nat. Hist.*, **91**: 1–232.

———. 1949 a. Continents in the Age of Mammals. *Tulsa Geol. Soc. Digest,* **17**: 58–65.

———. 1949 b. *The Meaning of Evolution.* Yale University Press, New Haven. (Also abridged edition, Mentor Books, 1951.)

———. 1950. History of the Fauna of Latin America. *Amer. Scientist,* **38**: 361–389. (Reprinted as Ch. XI, *Science in Progress,* 7th Series.)

———. 1952. Probabilities of Dispersal in Geologic Time. *Bull. Amer. Mus. Nat. Hist.,* **99**: 163–176.

WOOD, A. E. 1950. Porcupines, Paleogeography, and Parallelism. *Evolution,* **4**: 87–98.

ZIMMERMAN, E. C. 1948. *Insects of Hawaii.* Vol. 1. Introduction. Univ. Hawaii Press, Honolulu.

• • •

# PART 5

*Popularly, the mammals of Australia are often thought to consist only of marsupials, such as the kangaroos, koala and wombats. While this order does dominate the subcontinental fauna, there are a large number of interesting placental mammals as well, mostly rodents and bats, plus the extraordinary and primitive monotremes.*

*The author examines the whole mammalian make-up of Australia, past and present, in detail, and probes its relationships with the rest of the world, and what those relationships imply.*

• • •

# Historical Zoogeography of Australian Mammals

The exceptional evolutionary interest of islands has been universally recognized ever since, and indeed even before, general acceptance of the truth of evolution. Darwin and the Galápagos Islands at once rise to mind, along with a host of subsequent studies on, for example, the East Indies, the West Indies, Hawaii, and Madagascar. Nowhere else is the interplay of migration, isolation, and local radiation so clearly displayed. The peculiarities of insular faunas, usually impoverished and unbalanced in comparison with continental faunas, involve special ecological factors. In detail, other special evolutionary phenomena are strikingly displayed, for example the founder principle (Mayr, 1942) and convergence.

Many insular phenomena are rather closely correlated with the sizes of the islands concerned. When the islands approach and reach continental size, those phenomena become more complex and more difficult to interpret, but also richer and on a grander scale. All the continents (even Europe as distinct from Asia) have themselves been islands at one time or another. Only for Australia and South America, however, was strong isolation recent enough and sufficiently long-continued to be reflected by fully developed and extensive insular phenomena in the recent faunas. That is, of course, one of the best known zoogeographic facts, already emphasized by Wallace and familiar in even elementary treatments of zoology ever since.

The case of the mammals of South America, with abundant fossil evidence, has been analyzed both broadly and in considerable detail (in Part 6 of this book and references there). Equal or perhaps even more attention has been paid to the insularity of the Australian mammalian fauna. There, however, a satisfactory overall treatment of the whole problem has not recently been attempted. The fossil evidence is exiguous, and most of the historical zoogeographic studies of the recent fauna have been either so general as to lack significant detail or so partial and confined to particular groups and areas as to give an inadequate grasp of the whole. The purpose of the present essay is to supply that need, even though in an incomplete and inconclusive way. The attempt is made to place the data on mammals of the whole Australian Region available in previous publications by others into a tentative picture of the historical zoogeography of Australia. For this purpose the mammalian fauna of Australia proper (with Tasmania) is taken as a unit, and local distributions within the continent, affected as much by ecological as by strictly historical factors, are usually ignored.

## GENERAL NATURE OF THE FAUNA

Two of the usual characteristics of insular faunas, impoverishment and endemicity, are evident in the general makeup of the Australian fauna as summarized in the table below. Both factors vary with categorical level. The numbers of species (not given in the table) and of genera are not much smaller than would be expected from the size and environmental ecology of Australia. The number of orders, only five, is, however, even below that of Madagascar, with six. On other continents it ranges from seven * in Europe to twelve each in Asia and Africa.

* The order Primates is not counted in Europe, where it is represented only by man and the highly marginal Gibraltar monkeys, or in Australia. Native Artiodactyla, recently extinct in Madagascar, are counted there but Tubulidentata are not.

The idea of Australia as the land of marsupials and monotremes has been so much stressed that even some technical studies have overlooked the fact that Australia does have a rich placental fauna. In fact over half the native orders and families of Australia and

AUSTRALIAN NATIVE RECENT MAMMALS

| | FAMILIES | | GENERA | |
|---|---|---|---|---|
| | *No.** | *Endemic* † | *No.** | *Endemic* † |
| Monotremata | 2 | 100% | 2 | 100% |
| Marsupialia | 6 | 100% | 47 | 100% |
| Chiroptera | 7 | 0% | 21 | 29% |
| Rodentia | 1 | 0% | 13 | 77% |
| Carnivora | 1 | 0% | 1 | 0% |
| Totals | 17 | 47% | 84 | 67% |

* The numbers refer to inhabitants of continental Australia and Tasmania (and not the whole Australian Region).

† Groups are counted as endemic if confined to the region east of Wallace's line.

nearly half the native genera are placentals. The idea is, however, correct in a way, because the placentals are either of comparatively recent introduction or of only two broad adaptive types (bats and rats). The great majority of ecological niches for land mammals are, indeed, filled by marsupials. The frequent insular characteristic of faunal imbalance is hardly evident in Australia because the ancient, spectacular marsupial radiation has produced an essentially balanced fauna of land mammals within that one order.*

* Someone has remarked that if Linnaeus had been an Australian he would classify marsupials as from three to six orders rather than one. It is true that the ordinal poverty of Australia is to some extent an artifact of traditional classification, but the marsupials do seem to be a more compact and more closely related group than any three placental orders covering a comparable ecological range.

The broad outlines of placental zoogeography in the Australian Region are nevertheless more complex and in some ways more interesting than for the marsupials.

Endemicity varies not only categorically but also taxonomically. It is complete from specific through subclass levels for monotremes and through superfamily level for marsupials. It is nearly but not quite complete for species of rodents, and near three-quarters for genera, but the single family is not endemic. For bats, specific and generic endemicity is considerable but is decidedly less than for rodents, and none of the seven families is endemic. The one (placental) carnivore is not endemic at any level above the species.

The differences in endemicity reflect the fact that ancestral members of the various orders reached Australia at different times and in different ways, and that rates of evolution have also differed. In these respects each order is a separate case, and they will be separately discussed, with the sequence reversed from that usual in classification.

## CARNIVORA

It is well known that the only placental carnivore in Australia at the time of European discovery was the dingo. It interbreeds freely with domesticated dogs and resembles them more than it does any wild species. The general assumption is that dingos are feral descendants of domesticated or semidomesticated dogs introduced by aboriginal humans, although the archaeological evidence seems to be inadequate or ambiguous. If the assumption is correct, which is probable, this would be a unique case of a population that had passed through a phase of domestication and some degree of artificial selection and then had fully returned to the status of a wild species through many generations in isolation. (That is not really true of, for example, the "wild" horses of the American West.) Such a history may have had unusual genetic and adaptive consequences. Unfortunately it is probably too late to investigate that possibility adequately.

## RODENTIA

The numerous species of native rodents in the Australian Region all belong to the family Muridae. They have been studied in most detail by Tate (especially 1951), and with some later changes his data are the main basis for the following discussion. A few Pleistocene or early Recent fossils are known, but as far as yet studied they add virtually nothing of significance. From a historical point of view the recent murids can be divided into four broad groups:

I. Local members of the very widespread genus *Rattus.*

II. Old Papuan genera. Nine genera on New Guinea, two of which also occur in Australia.

III. The *Pseudomys* group. Eight genera, almost confined to Australia.

IV. The subfamily Hydromyinae. Nine genera in New Guinea, one in Australia, and one common to both.

These four groups have had different histories, and each is rather complex within itself.

I. *Rattus.* The now ubiquitous species *R. rattus* and *R. norvegicus,* along with *Mus musculus,* were introduced into the Australian Region after the European discovery. Rats of the *R. exulans* group are widely distributed in the Pacific in a way consistent with prehistoric (i.e., pre-European) spread by native canoes and difficult or impossible to explain otherwise. It is in accord with that mode of introduction that the group is well established in New Guinea, which is more in the prehistoric seafaring lanes, and is comparatively rare and marginal in Australia.

Besides these introductions, late and early, there are seventeen species of *Rattus,* nine in Australia, five in New Guinea, and three in both, that are endemic to the region and seem also to be autochthonous in it. Their differentiation there implies considerable antiquity and pre-human immigration of their ancestry. Tate places them in two of his "divisions" and eight of his "groups" of species of *Rattus,* but all could have differentiated from two or, less likely, from one ancestry migrant through the East Indies. From the degree of differentiation, arrival in New Guinea and hence in Australia could hardly have been much later than early Pleistocene. There has been some limited later Pleistocene or early Recent intermigration between New Guinea and Australia, with *R. ruber* and *gestri* probably moving from Australia to New Guinea and *R. leucopus* probably in the reverse direction.

II. "Old Papuans." *Uromys* and *Melomys,* common to Australia and New Guinea, and *Xenuromys* and *Pogonomelomys,* confined to New Guinea, comprise a group (the "*Uromys* group") of related rats all of which could well have been derived within New Guinea from a single ancestry near or in *Rattus.* Generic differentiation suggests that the ancestry probably reached New Guinea not later than the Pliocene. *Uromys* and *Melomys,* both of which have speciated widely in New Guinea, almost certainly originated there and spread later to Australia. *Melomys* migrated earlier, for it is now widespread in northern and eastern Australia and has developed new species there. *Uromys caudimaculatus,* not specifically distinct from its Papuan relatives and confined to northeastern Australia, must be a comparatively recent migrant. Within this group only lowland and chiefly rain forest forms spread from New Guinea to Australia, and there seems to have been no back migration.

There are five other old Papuan genera endemic in New Guinea: *Mallomys, Hyomys, Anisomys, Pogonomys,* and *Macruromys.* They are not especially related among themselves, aside from all being murids, and seem to have no special relatives elsewhere. They are even more distinct than the *Uromys* group and must be rather old, Pliocene, at least, and probably Miocene, in New Guinea and may represent several different invasions through the East Indies.

III. "Old Australians," or Pseudomyinae. These highly varied but related members of the *Pseudomys* group are the most common and characteristic native rats of Australia proper. They include the following main adaptive types:

1. Medium-sized to small, relatively unspecialized. Most abundant and diverse. *Pseudomys* (including *Thetomys* and *Gyomys,*

sometimes given generic rank), *Leggadina,* and *Zyzomys* (including *Laomys*).

2. Large, gregarious to colonial, nest-building, with very large ears. *Leporillus.*

3. Medium large, with short tail and slender feet. *Mastacomys.*

4. Small to moderate in size, with long ears, tail, and feet, saltorial. *Notomys.*

5. Very large, arboreal, with long, hairy tail. *Mesembriomys.*

6. Large to medium in size, eyes large and ears long, hopping, with long hind feet. *Conilurus.*

Among themselves these related forms represent a well-marked adaptive radiation which has produced a variety of animals convergent toward several different groups of rodents and rodentlike animals of other continents: true rats and mice (*Pseudomys* and allies), voles (*Mastacomys*), kangaroo rats or jerboas (*Notomys*), squirrels (*Mesembriomys*), and rabbits (*Conilurus*). In addition, one group (*Leporillus*) is fairly unique, not closely convergent toward any other rodents. Although this is a broad gamut for one small group of genera, it is far from occupying all the ecological niches of rodents on other continents.

In spite of their diversity, all these animals could have been derived from one ancestral immigrant. The degree of divergence, most or all of which seems to have occurred within Australia, demands a remote date for that ancestry, probably no later than Miocene but probably also little or no earlier, as true Muridae are not known anywhere before the Miocene. The ancestor must have been a very primitive murid, perhaps before distinct differentiation of the Murinae. Recognition of this group as a distinct subfamily, Pseudomyinae, seems warranted.

The pseudomyine ancestors were probably the first rodents ever to reach Australia proper. Their adaptive radiation then occurred there in the absence of any placental competitors. It seems possible that they replaced some earlier rodentlike marsupials, and it will be interesting to see whether such marsupials appear in the now unknown Australian Oligocene fauna.

Tate apparently tended to think of early rodent colonizations of Australia and New Guinea as separate phenomena, but all Australian rodents certainly came ancestrally from the East Indies or ultimately the mainland of Asia, and it seems highly probable that all reached Australia by way of New Guinea. The only likely alternative route is from Timor to Australia, and Mayr (1944 a) has shown that some birds followed that route. However, there are no non-introduced murids on Timor, and although the East Indies–Timor–Australia route is shorter it involves now, and probably did in the Miocene, stronger barriers to migration of land animals.

It seems probable that the pseudomyine ancestors were, like the "old Papuans," early migrants to and through New Guinea. If so, the lineage either died out in New Guinea after reaching Australia or is just possibly represented by the Papuan endemic genus *Lorentzimys.* Tate believed that *Lorentzimys,* a small mouselike or *Leggadina*-like murid, belongs in the *Pseudomys* group, although the not very detailed resemblance could be convergent. If *Lorentzimys* really is especially related to *Pseudomys* (and *Leggadina*), it is at least as probable that it is a survivor of ancestral Papuan pre-pseudomyines as that it was a migrant from Australia to New Guinea.

A single species of *Conilurus* has spread, certainly in late Pleistocene or Recent times, from northern Australia to southern New Guinea.

IV. Hydromyinae. This peculiar subfamily is characterized by basined cheek teeth and reduction or loss of the posterior molars. Of its eleven adequately established genera, nine are confined to New Guinea: *Leptomys, Paraleptomys, Pseudohydromys, Microhydromys, Baiyankamys, Parahydromys, Crossomys, Neohydromys,* and *Mayermys.* Another, *Hydromys,* has a species, *H. chrysogaster,* common to New Guinea and Australia. Although the species is now widespread in Australia, the Australian and New Guinean populations are not clearly sub-specifically distinct and must represent a quite recent spread from New Guinea.

*Xeromys,* a divergently specialized member of the subfamily, is confined to a small area in Queensland, Australia. Tate (1951) considered it "a localized invader from New Guinea during middle Pleistocene time or earlier." That is possible but improbable. The genus has no special, close relatives in New Guinea, and differentiation from surviving New Guinea hydromyines would probably have taken a longer time than since middle or even early Pleistocene. Its distribution suggests a relict rather than a localized invader, and it is probably an early offshoot of Papuan hydromyine ancestry that reached Australia in the Miocene or Pliocene and became divergently specialized there.

*Chrotomys* and the probably not distinct *Celaenomys* of the Philippine Islands (Luzon) are usually referred to the Hydromyinae. Raven (1935) believed that the subfamily originated in the Philippines and migrated hence to New Guinea and eventually Australia. Tate (1936) first suggested that the subfamily arose in Asia and migrated separately to the Philippines and through the East Indies to New Guinea and Australia. Later (Tate, 1951), he said that the Philippine forms are "possibly descendants of protohydromyines left along the ancient migration route from Asia to Australia." None of the three suggestions is satisfactory. The Philippines are quite remote from the (usual) Asia–East Indies–New Guinea–Australia route and no (other?) land mammals are known ever to have migrated in either direction between the Philippines and New Guinea. Nothing like the hydromyines now occurs anywhere in Asia or the East Indies.

I think it practically certain that *Chrotomys* is convergent toward the Hydromyinae and is of quite different ancestry within the Muridae. It is sharply distinct, as Tate says, "independently specialized," from ("other") hydromyines. The Philippine *Crunomys,* still less like a hydromyine, is roughly intermediate betwen *Chrotomys* and true Murinae and suggests a line of independent derivation from the latter. The South American *Ichthyomys* resembles *Hydromys* at least as closely as does *Chrotomys.* This is certainly a case of convergence, and it shows that the degree of resemblance between *Chrotomys* and the Hydromyinae could readily arise by convergence.

Everything points to the conclusion that the Hydromyinae, as such, originated not in Asia, in the Philippines, or along the East Indian island steppingstones but in New Guinea itself. The remote ancestry, necessarily near the base of the Muridae and possibly even in pre-murid cricetids, doubtless was Asiatic and migrated through the East Indies, and hydromyine specialization was Papuan. In New Guinea the group had an adaptive radiation analogous to that of the Pseudomyinae in Australia but different and more limited in ecological scope. About half of the genera, including those apparently most primitive (e.g., *Leptomys*) are terrestrial, some of them rather shrewlike. Adaptation to subaquatic and aquatic habits occurred within the subfamily radiation. That adaptation added other convergences, notably toward muskrats and some other aquatic rodents.

Summary on Muridae. The murids of the Australian Region clearly did not reach there over a land bridge but by island-hopping down the East Indian chain. From some time in the Miocene (perhaps but less probably even in late Oligocene) there was probably continual, intermittent drift of murids down that chain. There must have been marked attenuation, with fewer originally Asiatic lineages represented at increasing distances from the mainland. There was local differentiation on various islands along the route, and such differentiation was passed on, in part, to the next steppingstone and eventually to Australia, where final and in some cases most extensive differentiation occurred. Most and probably all of the Australian stocks passed through New Guinea, with varying degrees of differentiation there before spreading onward to Australia. In some instances that differentiation was less than specific; in others it was subfamilial. Although continual, the migrations may be analyzed into three successive waves:

A. Oldest wave, mainly or wholly Miocene. There was some basic radiation in New Guinea but this wave of invasions was evidently multiple, including up to seven but probably fewer different stocks already phylogenetically distinct before or while passing along the East Indies. Five of these stocks (the "old Papuans") remain endemic in New Guinea. Another radiated there into the Hydromyinae, one lineage (*Xeromys*) of which reached Australia early and another (within *Hydromys*) late. Another stock, the Pseudomyinae, although probably of old Papuan origin, had its major radiation in Australia. A single late species reached New Guinea from Australia.

B. Intermediate wave, probably Pliocene. This involved the probably single stock that evolved into the *Uromys* group in New Guinea. Spread thence to Australia involved first *Melomys* and later *Uromys*.

C. Late wave, Pleistocene or perhaps in part late Pliocene. This involved perhaps only one but probably two partly differentiated lineages of East Indian *Rattus*. It radiated moderately in New Guinea and quickly spread to Australia where it radiated more extensively at the specific level. In the late Pleistocene to Recent there was some further, but quite limited, interchange both ways between New Guinea and Australia. (Human introductions, both prehistoric and historic, followed.)

Throughout, predominant movement has evidently been from smaller East Indian islands to the great island of New Guinea and then from New Guinea to the still greater continent of Australia. That apparently violates the zoogeographic principle that successful colonization tends to go from larger and more varied to smaller and less varied regions. The principle strictly applies, however, to movement into essentially closed communities. Here the predominant tendency was to move from what were, for these animals, more closed to more open communities. Moreover, the stocks involved, although not precisely in the form in which they arrived, were ultimately derived from the largest and most varied land mass of all. In the broad picture, this is another example of the usual sort of spread from central, major masses to marginal and terminal areas. (See Darlington, 1957.)

## CHIROPTERA

Data for the bats of the Australian Region have also been taken mainly from Tate (1946), but again with some emendations from

CHIROPTERA OF AUSTRALIA AND THEIR EXTENSIONS BEYOND AUSTRALIA PROPER

| | *Australia and Tasmania* | *New Guinea Island* | *Other islands (into East Indies)* | *Asiatic mainland or beyond* |
|---|---|---|---|---|
| Megachiroptera | | | | |
| Pteropidae | | | | |
| Pteropinae | X | X | X | X |
| *Pteropus* | X | X | X | X |
| *Dobsonia* | X | X | | |
| *Nyctimene* | X | X | X | |
| Macroglossinae | X | X | X | X |
| *Macroglossus* | X | X | X | X |
| *Syconicteris* | X | X | X | |
| Microchiroptera | | | | |
| Emballonuridae | X | X | X | X |
| *Taphozous* | X | X | X | X |
| *Mormopterus* | X | X | X | X |
| Megadermatidae | X | X | X | X |
| *Macroderma* | X | | | |
| Rhinolophidae | X | X | X | X |
| *Rhinolophus* | X | X | X | X |
| Hipposideridae | X | X | X | X |
| *Rhinonicteris* | X | | | |
| *Hipposideros* | X | X | X | X |
| Vespertilionidae | X | X | X | X |
| *Nyctophilus* | X | X | X | |
| *Eptesicus* | X | X | X | X |
| *Pipistrellus* | X | X | X | X |
| *Chalinolobus* | X | X | X | X |
| *Myotis* | X | X | X | X |
| *Scoteinus* | X | X | X | X |
| *Phoniscus* | X | X | X | X |
| *Miniopterus* | X | X | X | X |
| *Kerivoula* | X | X | X | X |
| Molossidae | X | X | X | X |
| *Nyctinomus* | X | | X | X |

later studies.† The families and genera here recognized in Australia and Tasmania are listed above, and data on endemicity for genera and for Tate's species groups in each family are given.

ENDEMICITY IN AUSTRALIAN BATS *

| Families | Genera | | |
|---|---|---|---|
| | *Aus.* | *Aus. R.* | *Aus.–O.* |
| Pteropidae | 0 | 3 | 2 |
| Emballonuridae | 0 | 0 | 2 |
| Megadermatidae | 1 | 0 | 0 |
| Rhinolophidae | 0 | 0 | 1 |
| Hipposideridae | 1 | 0 | 1 |
| Vespertilionidae | 0 | 1 | 8 |
| Molossidae | 0 | 0 | 1 |
| Totals | 2(10%) | 4(19%) | 15(71%) |
| Aus. R. total | 6(29%) | | |
| Aus. total | 21 | | |

| Families | Species Groups | | |
|---|---|---|---|
| | *Aus.* | *Aus. R.* | *Aus.–O.* |
| Pteropidae | 0 | 7 | 3 |
| Emballonuridae | 1 | 1 | 1 |
| Megadermatidae | 1 | 0 | 0 |
| Rhinolophidae | 1 | 2 | 3 |
| Hipposideridae | 1 | 1 | 3 |
| Vespertilionidae | 1 | 3 | 8 |
| Molossidae | 1 | 0 | 1 |
| Totals | 6(15%) | 14(36%) | 19(49%) |
| Aus. R. total | 20(51%) | | |
| Aus. total | 39 | | |

* Only groups that occur in Australia (and Tasmania) are considered. Aus. = Australia only. Aus. R. = Australian Region (including New Guinea, adjacent islands, and East Indies east of Wallace's line). Aus.–O. = Australian Region into Oriental Region or beyond (including East Indies west of Wallace's line). Numbers in the table are of genera and of species groups as in Tate (1946), slightly modified.

† Some of the later changes in the literature have consisted merely of giving generic names to some of Tate's species and species groups, without further study. Those changes from Tate's arrangement have not been justified by new evidence, and some of them are open to ethical objections. In general, I have not adopted them.

The seven chiropteran families of Australia proper are all widespread in Eurasia and, for some of them, other continents, and all are old. No fossils have been described from the Australian region, but all these families date as far back as middle Eocene to middle Oligocene in Europe. The fossils are few, and in fact all these families undoubtedly existed in the Eocene, and some may have originated in the Paleocene. They could, then, have reached Australia at any time since the early Tertiary, and there has been no differentiation of families and comparatively little of genera in the Australian Region.

The lower endemicity in comparison with the Muridae must be related to the greater ability of bats—flying animals—to cross water barriers. There are no strongly marked ecological barriers, aside from the water gaps, on the route from southeast Asia through the East Indies to New Guinea. All the islands are in the same climatic zone and most of them have considerable resemblance or, at least, overlap in other ecological conditions. The importance of that factor for Chiroptera is evident from comparison with the Neotropical Region. Although there is now no water barrier between the Neotropical and Nearctic Regions, the ecological barrier for bats is so marked that 56% of Neotropical families are endemic, as against none in Australia, and 87% of the Neotropical genera are endemic, as against only 29% in Australia. Bat distribution resembles that of birds and of many plants more than that of terrestrial mammals.

The Australian bats are much more diverse than the rodents, and, in sharp contrast to the latter, they represent an only moderately attenuated sampling of the whole of the original mainland Asiatic fauna. They do not fall into definite groups or waves as regards antiquity in the Australian Region but seem to have filtered in continuously throughout most of the Cenozoic. There is a wide spectrum of endemicity, which may be assumed to be approximately but only approximately correlated with antiquity in the region. Some Australian species, e.g., in *Myotis, Pipistrellus,* and *Miniopterus,* are very close to Indian, European, and even African species, although supposedly not quite identical. On the other hand there are a few clear-cut endemic Australian genera, notably the peculiar *Macroderma,* which is a predator on other bats. As is evident from the table above, the fruit bats or Megachiroptera (Pteropidae), although less diversified, are much more divergent in the Australian Region, much higher in endemicity, than the Microchiroptera (the six other families). That suggests that the fruit bats are on an average older than the other bats in this region, although the first entry of microchiropterans may have been quite as early as or earlier than that of the megachiropterans.

In spite of the absence of endemicity above the generic level, first colonizations could have been and probably were quite early in the Cenozoic. The antiquity of the families in Europe has been mentioned, and in spite of the paucity of fossil record even a living genus (*Rhinolophus*) now present in the Australian Region is reported from the Eocene of Europe. The total number of colonizations from the East Indies into the Australian Region has not been estimated, but it must have been large, on the order of twenty or thirty, possibly even more. The basic radiations, those now at family and in good part also generic level, occurred in Eurasia. There has been little true radiation in the Australian Region, but mostly local geographic differentiation below the generic level. The center of density in the region is not on the Australian continent but on the islands from New Guinea to the Solomons, where there are more groups of bats than in Australia proper. Only two of the twenty-one Australian genera and six of the thirty-nine species groups are confined to Australia. What regional differentiation there is clearly took place mostly in the islands (in part also the East Indian islands) before the groups reached continental Australia. Nevertheless two sharply distinct groups (*Macroderma* and *Rhinonicteris*) have originated in Australia, and most groups have become subspecifically to specifically distinct since reaching there.

For the bats, as for birds and such other animals as have spread along the whole chain, there is a gradient between the Asiatic and the Australian mainlands. Tate (1946) divided his species groups of bats according to assumed Asiatic or Australian regional origin, in a somewhat arbitrary way but using criteria of greatest distinction or differentiation, abundance, and presence of relatives toward one end or the other of the sequence. Some of his data on that basis are given in the upper part of the next table. He envisioned the gradients as representing two sequences of counter-migrations, one from Asia toward the Australian Region and one from the Australian Region toward Asia, both currents becoming more and more attenuated with greater distance from their assumed regions of origin. The same approach is implicit in earlier studies by Mayr (1944 b)* and others, and it seems to be rather generally accepted.

That approach is certainly oversimplified, as has been realized by those who nevertheless followed it. It would not be a serious oversimplification for groups that did in fact have their basic differentiation and the origins of most of their taxa either in Asia or in Australia. That is true, for example, of marsupials, with virtually all taxa of Australian origin, as compared with placentals exclusive of bats and Muridae, with virtually all taxa of Asiatic origin. As suggested in Fig. 35, those groups do show just the kind of overlap and opposite attenuations involved in the counter-migration hypothesis.

That hypothesis is, however, an unjustified oversimplification when applied to the bats. For them there are not two clear-cut and quite distinct centers of origin from which counter-migrations occurred. All the families, most of the genera (about 90%), and an undertermined but probably large number of the species groups of Australian bats originated outside that region, i.e., in the Oriental Region or beyond. The predominant pertinent movement was not in two counter-migrations, but in one direction, from Asia toward Australia. It thus seems probable that a significant element in the Australia–Asia gradient was increasing divergence or differentiation of animals really spreading in the opposite direction (Asia–Australia). During that movement they evolved progressively, in greatest part below the generic level, away from their Asiatic ancestry. The most impressive argument against that conclusion is that faunas of intermediate islands are impoverished in comparison with either end of the sequence, and that ancestral forms or close rela-

* Mayr's analyses did not include the bats, Tate's data being then not yet available.

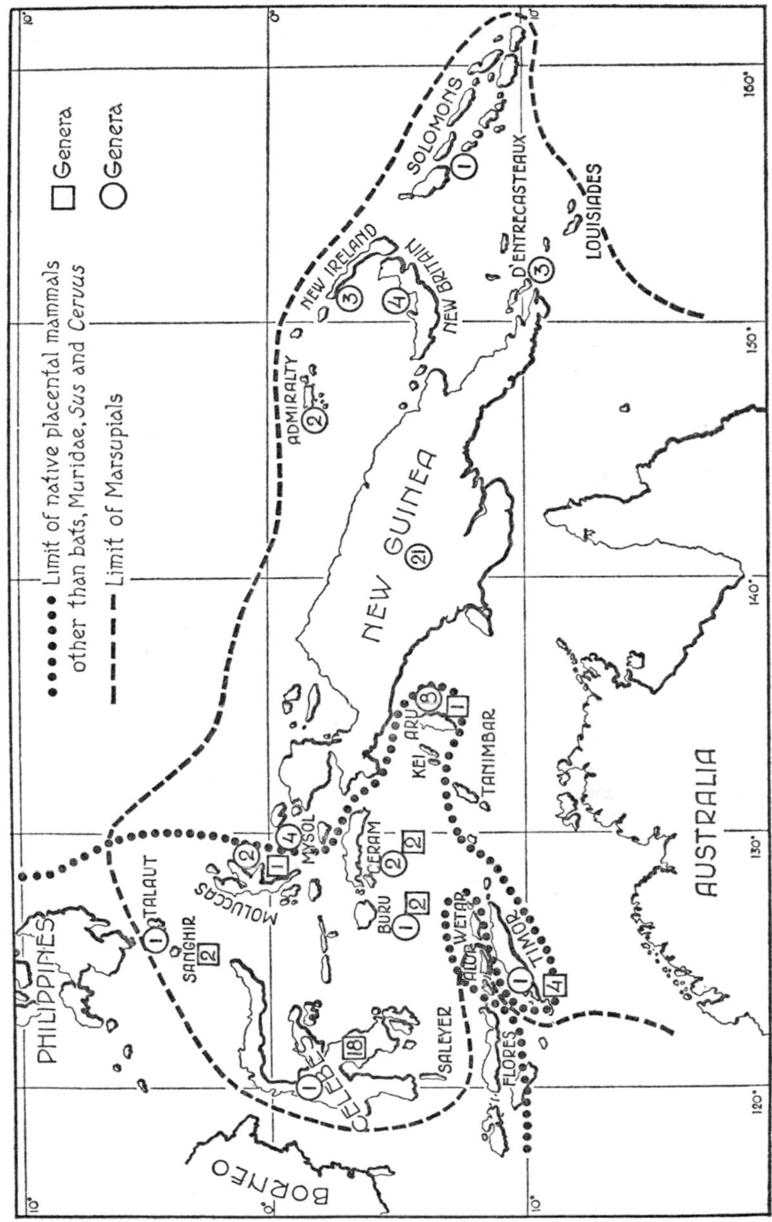


Fig. 35. Islands of the Australian Region, with numbers of genera and limits reached by marsupials and by native placentals other than bats, murids, and probable late human introductions of pigs and deer.

tives of many Australian species groups do not now occur in the Oriental Region. However, ancestors of those groups certainly did migrate through the islands even where relatives are now absent, and survival in the Oriental Region of recognizably close collaterals from the ancestry would not be expected in all or in many instances for migrations that started in the early Tertiary.*

On that hypothesis, the double sets of taxonomic clines of Tate and others are in fact a single set of genetic clines, with similarities decreasing and differences increasing in the one direction: Asia–Australia. By itself, that hypothesis is certainly also oversimple. There doubtless was also some counter-migration, involving low taxa, in the direction Australia–Asia. It must also be remembered that the principal eastern center of origin and dispersal was not Australia itself but New Guinea. There must moreover have been further low-level complications by origins and dispersals in various directions around other points scattered along the sequence.

The distributional facts can be more objectively shown by measures of actually existing faunal resemblances, which do not involve any hypotheses as to the places of origin of the various taxa. That approach is exemplified in the lower part of the table below. The figures show that if one starts at either more or less terminal area (continental East Indian islands; Australia and its continental islands), faunal resemblances become less with increasing distance. The measurement of that change has special interest for the particular case, but certainly the result is not surprising. The trend shown would almost inevitably appear (with different intensities)

* Comparatively small East Indian islands would be saturated with bats by a smaller number of stocks than those that reached the Australian Region and survived there. Later movements down the island chain could then occur only by the extinction (competitive or not) of earlier migrants on the smaller islands. Thus in spite of attenuation within each faunal wave and in spite of more westward islands having had larger totals of stocks through all time, at any one time (such as the present) each of the smaller islands would have a smaller number than had passed through it and survived in the Australian Region at the given time. It would also be precisely the earlier ancestral migrants, hence those whose descendants are now most distinctive in the Australian Region, that would have become extinct on the smaller intermediate East Indian islands.

TAXONOMIC GRADIENTS OF CHIROPTERA BETWEEN THE EAST INDIES AND AUSTRALIA

I. Percentages of species groups of supposed Asiatic and Australian (Region) origin, after Tate (1946).

| *"Origin"* | *Celebes* | *Moluccas* | *Australia* | *New Guinea and Solomons* |
|---|---|---|---|---|
| Asia | 90% | 64% | 35% | 32% |
| Australian Region | 10% | 34% | 65% | 68% |

II. Indices of faunal resemblances, 100 $C/N_1$ (see Simpson, 1960 b), for species groups between the following areas:

A, East Indies, from Asia to edge of Asiatic continental shelf (modified Wallace's line; see Mayr, 1944 b).

B, islands between A and C.

C, Australia and islands on its continental shelf (nearly but not quite to Weber's line; see Mayr, 1944 b).

Raw data from Tate (1946):

| | A-B | A-C | C-A | C-B |
|---|---|---|---|---|
| 100 $C/N_1$ | 58 | 31 | 31 | 53 |

in comparisons of *any* two faunas with each other and with intermediate faunas. That result would arise in each of three models that are extreme or limiting cases and are not to be expected in pure, uncomplicated form in nature:

1. Counter-migrations between two areas originally with faunas completely different at the taxonomic levels under consideration.
2. Migration of the whole fauna from one terminal area to the other with progressive evolution along the way.
3. Local differentiation throughout a fauna that was originally uniform in and between the two areas.

In most cases of real faunas, all three factors probably act and interact, plus additional local perturbations and complications. That is doubtless true of the faunal relationships between the Oriental and Australian Regions. As regards the non-flying land mammals, the first factor predominates in the comparatively small area of overlap (Aru to Celebes). As regards the bats, such dominance of any one factor is less clear, but the second factor is probably at least as important as either of the other two.

For the bats, both Tate's counter-migration approach and the present approach by objective faunal resemblance place the 50-50 line, or faunal balance line, or Weber's line, east of the Moluccas rather than west of them, as has been calculated for several other groups of animals (Mayr, 1944 b, and references there). It is only to be expected that different groups will differ somewhat in this respect, and all groups so far analyzed do agree in placing this significant line well to the east of Wallace's line.

## MARSUPIALIA

On the scale of this study, the distribution of the Australian marsupials is much simpler than that of the Muridae or Chiroptera. It has also been the subject of more reviews as well as detailed studies (e.g., and just by way of a few examples among many: Carter, Hill, and Tate, 1945; Laurie and Hill, 1954; Tate, 1952; Troughton, 1947). It will therefore be more briefly treated here.

In contrast with the Muridae and Chiroptera, there are some pertinent but still grossly inadequate fossil data for the marsupials. The Pleistocene to sub-Recent fauna of Australia, as on other continents, was richer than the present fauna, and it was already rather well-known in the 19th century (full lists and older literature in Simpson, 1930; later lists down to genera for both fossil and recent faunas in Simpson, 1945). Information on earlier mammals is still extremely scanty. Only about a dozen forms, scattered from late Eocene or Oligocene through the Pliocene, have as yet been described and not all of those are well identified.* (See Gill, 1957; Stirton, 1955, 1957 a, 1957 b). All belong to Pleistocene or Recent families. As far as they go, they suggest that there has been some progression at generic and specific levels, but that the general character of the Australian marsupial fauna did not change significantly from the mid-Tertiary, at latest, into the Pleistocene.

In conservative classification there are six living and two recently

* The University of California group has other materials, partly studied by Stirton and Tedford but not yet published.

extinct families of Australian marsupials. A single species of *Phalanger* reaches Celebes and thus extends into an area not now usually included in the Australian Region (but still east of Wallace's line). With that trivial exception, all the marsupials of the Australian Region are endemic through the superfamily level. The major radiation clearly took place on the Australian continent and is surely very old. Scanty as it is, the fossil evidence strongly suggests that the families, and probably some or all subfamilies, were differentiated by the Miocene at latest, and probably much earlier. (The majority of Recent mammalian families in the rest of the world were differentiated in the Eocene and Oligocene; marsupial families may prove to be even older.)

From Australia marsupials have spread with a completely regular pattern of progressive attenuation (Fig. 35) as far as the Solomons to the northeast, Talaut to the north, and Celebes to the west. Four families and twenty-one genera occur in New Guinea, as listed in the table below. Most of the Papuan species and six of the genera are not present in Australia proper. Spread of their ancestors to New Guinea must have begun far back in the Tertiary, and there has evidently been some intermittent interchange ever since. Even though it has developed autochthonous genera, New Guinea has apparently not been a major center for marsupial evolution, as it was for both rats and bats. Nevertheless four genera shared with Australia perhaps evolved in New Guinea and may represent back-migration in Australia: the bandicoot *Echymipera,* the phalangers ("possums" to Australians) *Phalanger* and *Dactylopsila,* and the tree kangaroo *Dendrolagus.*

Ten of the Papuan genera have also spread to other islands. They thin out rapidly and regularly with increasing distance from New Guinea. The most successful are *Phalanger,* which occurs wherever there are any marsupials in the Australian Region (and, as noted, as far as Celebes), gliding phalangers of the genus *Petaurus,* and bandicoots of the genus *Echymipera.* Significantly, all are typically rain forest groups. Ceram has an endemic genus of bandicoots, *Rhynchomeles,* which is most closely related to the endemic Papuan *Peroryctes.* It is clear that spread of all these

MARSUPIALS OF NEW GUINEA *

Dasyuridae

I A *Phascogale* (including *Murexia, Antechinus, Neophascogale, Phascolosorex*)

I A *Sminthopsis*

A *Planigale*

I *Myoictis*

A *Dasyurus* (including *Satanellus*)

Peramelidae

*Peroryctes* }
*Microperoryctes* } near Australian *Perameles*

I A† *Echymipera*

A *Thylacis* (= *Isoodon*)

Phalangeridae

X A† *Phalanger* (including *Spilocuscus*)

A *Eudromicia*—near Australian *Cercaertus*

I A† *Dactylopsila*

*Dactylonax*—near Australian and Papuan *Dactylopsila*

I A *Petaurus*

A *Acrobates*

*Distoechurus*

A *Pseudocheirus*

Macropodidae

I A *Thylogale*

I A *Protemnodon* (= *Wallabia*)

A† *Dendrolagus*

I *Dorcopsis* (including *Dorcopsulis*)

* I—Extends also to nearby islands. A— Also of Australia and probably originated there. A†—Also on Australia but possibly originated on New Guinea. X—Coextensive with Marsupialia on islands.

groups to other islands has been from New Guinea and not directly from Australia. Even the Timor phalanger, *Phalanger orientalis,* although closer to Australia than to New Guinea, came from New Guinea, probably by way of Ceram, Buru, and Wetar. That species has spread from New Guinea in late Pleistocene or Recent times all over the islands that have marsupials, from the Solomons to Celebes, and also to Cape York Peninsula on Australia.

It is extremely unlikely that Australia had any non-flying land placentals before the arrival of murids, which, as has been indicated, was no earlier than Oligocene and probably in the Miocene. By that time the basic marsupial radiation had already occurred, and its very extent supports the conclusion that the early marsupials had no placental competitors. Marsupials, abundant in the late Cretaceous and early Tertiary of North America and the early Tertiary, at least, of Europe, there faced strong and varied placental competition and became extinct by the Miocene (although one species later reinvaded the Nearctic). In South America specialized placental insectivores, rodents, and specialized placental carnivores, all absent in the earliest Paleocene of North America, were not among the original stocks derived from North America, and in their absence the marsupials underwent a partial radiation including much convergence toward those placentals. In Australia there were presumably no earliest Tertitary placentals, and the marsupials underwent a radiation that was essentially complete ecologically.

The classical explanation for the absence of early placentals in Australia was that the marsupials evolved first and spread to that continent over a land bridge that was submerged before there were any placentals to cross it. Although that theory is still sometimes presented, it has long been abandoned by closer students of the problem. Marsupials and placentals, distinctly differentiated as such, apparently evolved at about the same time, and the earliest marsupials do not seem to have been significantly more primitive than the earliest placentals. The most reasonable explanation, although it is still speculative in the absence of any direct evidence, is that no land bridge was involved but that primitive marsupials reached the continent over a series of sea barriers. The original stock must have been of small, arboreal, opossumlike (i.e., didelphoid, not phalangeroid) animals such as would be particularly apt at island-hopping. Arrival of one pair or of a single gravid female in Australia could have sufficed. Subsequent extinction of marsupials in the East Indies (where fossil faunas that might include early marsupials are completely unknown), would be no more surprising than their known extinction in Eurasia.*

Under this theory, the placentals were excluded by the sequence of marine barriers that the marsupials crossed. That may have been because southeastern Asiatic placentals of that early time were less apt at island-hopping. Somewhat more likely is the hypothesis that the event was extremely improbable for either group and that selection of one group rather than another for the unique, improbable event was purely by chance (or was stochastic). As has been shown, similar events repeatedly occurred for one group of placentals, the murids, from about mid-Tertiary onward. Of South Asiatic mammals the murids (not yet in existence when the marsupials reached Australia) are clearly particularly well adapted for island-hopping. It is also possible that the barriers became somewhat less formidable around Miocene times.

The time of arrival of marsupials in Australia was probably late Cretaceous or Paleocene. There is suggestive although not wholly adequate evidence from North America and Europe that the marsupials were not clearly differentiated as such until the late Cretaceous. From the other direction, the great scope of marsupial radiation in Australia suggests very early arrival there. The earliest fossil marsupial known from Australia, *Wynyardia bassiana,* is of late Eocene or Oligocene age and already belonged to a somewhat specialized Recent family (Gill, 1957).†

A possible but on the whole considerably less probable theory is that pre-marsupial therians (perhaps some branch of the Pantotheria) reached Australia in the earlier Cretaceous, or even in the Jurassic, and there evolved in isolation into marsupials. In that case, also, the group island-hopped in the late Cretaceous but in the reverse direction, from Australia to Asia, whence it spread to Europe and to the Americas.

* No fossil marsupials have been found in Asia, but there, too, faunas that might include them are as yet very poorly known. Known presence of early marsupials in both Europe and North America makes it almost certain that they also occurred in Asia.

† Ride has since claimed that *Wynyardia* is more distinctive and primitive.

## MONOTREMATA

As is well known, the monotremes belong to two families—the Tachyglossidae with *Tachyglossus* on both Australia and New Guinea and its close ally *Zaglossus* on New Guinea only, and the Ornithorhynchidae with the single Australian genus. These are extreme endemics, representing a whole subclass now confined to the Australian Region. Universal recognition that they have some very primitive characters in comparison with other (or true) mammals has sometimes obscured the fact that in other respects they are extremely specialized, about as specialized as any mammals (or reptiles). The two families are also markedly divergent from each other and must have been separated for a very long time.

A few Australian Pleistocene fossils cast no light on the history of the group. In the rest of the world nothing possibly related to them is known in the late Mesozoic or the Cenozoic. The one possibly direct clue, a slender and equivocal one, is that the morganucodonts or eozostrodonts, known from the late Triassic of Great Britain, share a peculiarity of the ear region with the recent monotremes. On that account Kermack and Mussett (1958) have suggested that the morganucodonts are, or are near, the monotreme ancestry.* This is quite possible, but the enormous gap both in time and in known morphology makes it extremely tentative at present. The morganucodonts were probably a lineage from therapsids, nominal reptiles, that was acquiring mammalian structural status parallel to but quite separately from the contemporary ancestry of the Theria (that is, marsupials and placentals, together). It is also possible that they were an offshoot from the therian ancestry near the nominal reptile-mammal boundary. Regardless of the involvement of the morganucodonts, other less possibly direct but more abundant and compelling comparative anatomical evidence suggests that the monotremes were derived from the therapsids either quite separately from the therian ancestry or at most from near the very base of that ancestry at a stage equivocal in status between

* The suggestion has since been weakened.

reptiles and mammals. Whether they should, indeed, continue to be classified as mammals, which I consider still most convenient, becomes then a mere matter of definition (e.g., Simpson, 1960a).

The most probable present hypothesis on the geographic history of the monotremes is that advanced therapsids or early post-therapsids, near the arbitrary reptile-mammal line as usually drawn, reached Australia in the late Triassic or in the Jurassic, that they there gave rise to the monotremes of stricter definition, and that the latter have persisted in and have always been confined to the Australian Region. It is completely speculative, but is an interesting speculation, that there may have been a Mesozoic monotreme radiation in Australia that was mostly, yet not entirely, replaced by a later, mainly early Tertiary, marsupial radiation.

## FURTHER PROBLEMS

It is certainly not claimed that this study of the broadest aspects of the historical zoogeography of Australian mammals, departing from the basis of work by Tate and many others, is definitive. It does, however, seem improbable that this more general aspect of the subject can be carried much further on the basis of recent animals. What is needed to fill in detail and to check present hypotheses and speculations is fossil evidence. The dozen or so Tertiary mammals so far described, interesting as they are in detail, throw virtually no light on the broad problems. Especially needed are Miocene and Pliocene microfaunas including murids, any Tertiary faunas including bats, and Cretaceous-Paleocene faunas of marsupials. Intense efforts so far (e.g., by Stirton and his associates) have had quite limited success, but enough to encourage the belief that such faunas can eventually be found. Discoveries of early Tertiary faunas in southern Asia and the East Indies may also throw useful light on the Australian Region.

On mammalian distributions within Australia, not treated here, some suggestive work has been done, but less than on some other groups (e.g., certain birds, frogs), and more remains to be done. Here there are available rather extensive Pleistocene and sub-

Recent data, but there is great need for the discovery and collection of more small mammals, especially, of those ages. It may be salutary to point out that in North America the accumulation of Pleistocene-Recent data of that desirable sort is now enormous, and yet that the progress so far made on its evolutionary, historical, zoogeographical, and ecological interpretation is highly unsatisfactory.

## SUMMARY

1. The five orders of native Australian mammals have had characteristically different geographic histories.
2. The dingo, the only native placental carnivore, is probably a feral species of prehistoric human introduction.
3. The Muridae have made multiple invasions of the Australian Region from Asia across the steppingstones of the East Indian islands, beginning probably in the Miocene. An "old Papuan" group now includes five rather isolated genera in New Guinea. Another old Papuan stock evolved there into the peculiar subfamily Hydromyinae. There have been two spreads of hydromyines, one early and one late, from New Guinea into Australia. The supposed hydromyines of the Philippines are only convergent toward the true Hydromyinae.
4. A stock probably of old Papuan origin but not positively identified in New Guinea early reached Australia and radiated extensively there into the *Pseudomys* group of genera, which warrants recognition as a subfamily Pseudomyinae. There was one late invasion of this group into New Guinea.
5. A probably somewhat later (Pliocene?) migrant into New Guinea gave rise there to the *Uromys* group of four genera. Thence first *Melomys* and later *Uromys* reached Australia, with little further differentiation.
6. There was a later, late Pliocene or early Pleistocene, invasion of New Guinea by one or two partly differentiated lineages of *Rattus*. This stock speciated considerably in New Guinea, reached Australia, and speciated more widely there. Prehistoric and historic introductions by humans followed.

7. The bats of the Australian Region are more varied than the rodents but have less endemicity. All were also derived ultimately from Asia, where the basic differentiation occurred, in a long series of migrations, perhaps thirty or even more, from early Tertiary onward.

8. New Guinea was the major center for bat differentiation within the Australian Region, mainly at lower taxonomic levels. Repeated spread from New Guinea to Australia occurred. There was no extensive radiation in Australia, and new differentiation there was less than in New Guinea.

9. There is a fairly regular gradient of chiropteran faunal similarity from Asia through the East Indies to Australia. Migration was predominantly in the direction Asia–Australia, and the gradient is in part due to progressive evolution along that line, in part to subsequent counter-migration from New Guinea westward, and in part to more local differentiations and movements.

10. Marsupials probably reached Australia in the late Mesozoic or earliest Cenozoic by island-hopping through the East Indies, where they became extinct. The great, well-known marsupial radiation occurred in Australia. Numerous marsupials spread from Australia to New Guinea, where there was some further progressive differentiation but little true radiation. There was some back-migration from New Guinea to Australia. Continuously attenuated spread to other islands, as far as the Solomons, Talaut, and Celebes, occurred from New Guinea, not directly from Australia.

11. Ancestors of the monotremes, still near the nominal reptile-mammal line, probably reached Australia in the Jurassic or late Triassic and there evolved into the Monotremata, strictly speaking, which have probably never occurred outside the Australian Region.

## REFERENCES

CARTER, T. T., J. E. HILL, and G. H. H. TATE. 1945. *Mammals of the Pacific World.* Macmillan, New York.

DARLINGTON, P. J. 1957. *Zoogeography: The Geographic Distribution of Animals.* Wiley, New York.

GILL, E. D. 1957. The stratigraphical occurrence and paleoecology of some Australian Tertiary marsupials. *Mem. Nat. Mus. Victoria,* no. **21**: 135–203.

KERMACK, K. A., and F. MUSSETT. 1958. The jaw articulation of the Docodonta and the classification of Mesozoic mammals. *Proc. Roy. Soc.* London, B, **148**: 204–215.

LAURIE, E. M. O., and J. E. HILL. 1954. List of land mammals of New Guinea, Celebes, and adjacent islands. British Museum, London.

MAYR, E. 1944 a. Timor and the colonization of Australia by birds. *Emu,* **44**: 113–130.

———. 1944 b. Wallace's line in the light of recent zoogeographic studies. *Quart. Rev. Biol.,* **19**, 1–14.

RAVEN, H. C. 1935. Wallace's line and the distribution of Indo-Australian mammals. *Bull. Amer. Mus. Nat. Hist.,* **68**: 177–293.

SIMPSON, G. G. 1930. Fossilium catalogus. 1: Animalia. Part 47. Post-Mesozoic Marsupialia. W. Junk, Berlin.

———. 1945. The principles of classification and a classification of mammals. *Bull. Amer. Mus. Nat. Hist.,* **85**, i–xvi, 1–350.

———. 1950. History of the fauna of Latin America. *Amer. Scientist,* **38**: 361–389.

———. 1960 a. Diagnosis of the classes Mammalia and Reptilia. *Evolution,* **14**: 388–392.

———. 1960 b. Notes on the measurement of faunal resemblance. *Amer. Jour. Sci.,* **258A**: 300–311.

STIRTON, R. A. 1955. Late Tertiary marsupials from South Australia. *Records South Australian Mus.,* **11**: 247–268.

———. 1957 a. A new koala from the Palankarinna fauna of South Australia. *Records South Australian Mus.,* **13**: 71–81.

———. 1957 b. Tertiary marsupials from Victoria, Australia. *Mem. Nat. Mus. Victoria,* no. **21**: 121–134.

TATE, G. H. H. 1936. Some Muridae of the Indo-Australian region. *Bull. Amer. Mus. Nat. Hist.,* **72**: 501–728.

———. 1946. Geographical distribution of the bats in the Australian archipelago. *Amer. Mus. Novitates,* no. 1323.

———. 1951. The rodents of Australia and New Guinea. *Bull. Amer. Mus. Nat. Hist.,* **97**: 183–430.

———. 1952. Mammals of the Cape York Peninsula, with notes on the occurrence of rain forest in Queensland. *Bull. Amer. Mus. Nat. Hist.,* **98**: 563–616.

TROUGHTON, E. 1947. *Furred Animals of Australia.* Scribner's Sons, New York.

• • •

# PART 6

*As the previous essay examined Australia, so this one examines South America. Why a discrete Latin American mammalian fauna should exist at all is a question calling for an extended and thoughtful answer.*

*The curious and mostly extinct orders of mammals which actually originated in South America are studied in detail and the author deals with the part played by the Central American land bridges during various epochs.*

# History of the fauna of Latin America

It is odd that there should be *a* Latin American fauna, a broad unit that can be roughly designated by such a term as "Latin American," defined by human linguistics and culture. The animals inhabiting this area can hardly have foreseen that the dominant languages of the 20th century would here be Spanish and Portuguese or that the European cultural elements imported here would come mainly from Latin Europe—from Spain and Portugal and also, in considerable measure, from France and Italy. Nevertheless, there is a characteristic fauna that coincides approximately with Latin America and that differs in some major traits from the fauna of English-speaking America. The coincidence is not precise. The fauna of northern Mexico, although transitional in some respects, is more nearly allied to that of the United States than to that of most of Latin America. Exact correspondence of native fauna and imported culture would be a miracle, and it is still a wonder that the equivalence is as close as it really is. There is, indeed, a common factor that removes the correspondence from the realm of pure coincidence. The demarcation both of faunas and of cultures has been influenced by climatic factors.

Radical differences in the two major faunal realms of the Americas were noticed by the early explorers and are still obvious enough to the modern traveler. A New Englander traveling in Brazil does not need to be a zoologist to observe that the animals of that country are at least as exotic as are the speech and customs of its human inhabitants. He will see some animals which, although subtly different, look reasonably familiar to him: deer, foxes, field mice, squirrels, rabbits, and a few others. More will be completely new to him outside of zoos: peccaries, tapirs, jaguars, kinkajous, guinea pigs, agoutis, capybaras, armadillos, tree sloths, monkeys, and a host of others.

The distinction is not confined to mammals, a few of which have been named, but extends to all sorts of animals. The river rays, the lungfish, the piranhas, and many other freshwater fish are strange to northern eyes. The frogs and toads may look familiar at first sight, but on closer inspection such forms as the Surinam toad, incubating the young in its back, and, indeed, almost all others will be found distinctive. Among turtles, the matamata and other side-necked forms are obviously exotic, and so are the boa constrictors and numerous other snakes. The ostrichlike rheas and the wing-clawed hoatzins are only two among the numerous purely Latin American birds. Additions to the long roster could be provided among earthworms, insects, and innumerable others.

The fauna is by no means uniform all over Latin America, but it is evident, first, that broadly similar faunal characteristics do appear throughout most of this great area and, second, that these characteristics distinguish the region sharply from non-Latin North America or any other continent. These facts led the students of animal distribution in the latter half of the 19th century (the Sclaters, Wallace, Beddard, and Lydekker, to name some of the more eminent) to set Latin America aside as the Neotropical Region or Neogaea. In the classical arrangement, this region includes all of South America (even those parts decidedly nontropical), Central America, tropical Mexico (but not the temperate central plateau and northern Mexico), and the West Indies. Although the boundaries are sharp and definite on the map, it was of course recognized that the line in Mexico is not awesomely respected by the animals and that it really lies within a broad transition zone. Some mainly neotropical animals, such as the peccaries or jaguars, range into the United States far north of the map line. Some mainly nearctic (non-Latin North American) mammals, such as shrews, similarly range well south of the line. It has also long been recognized that the West Indian fauna is not typically or fully Latin American or neotropical. It is impoverished relative to the mainland, has its own peculiar forms, and has a few special resemblances to the North American fauna.

In spite of some ambiguities, the Neotropical Region does have a well-established clarity and validity in the zoogeography of the world as it exists today. This static picture is, however, the result of a long and dynamic historical process. The nature of the fauna in what is now designated as the Neotropical Region has changed radically during geological history. Different parts of that region have not had the same history. Faunal resemblances and distinctions have sometimes been greater, sometimes less than they are today. Boundaries of faunal assemblages have not remained in the same place. Recent neotropical elements may be old in that region or may be latecomers with their historical faunal associations elsewhere.

Until relatively recently, geologically speaking (well into the Pliocene), Central America had faunal affinities almost exclusively with North America and hardly at all with South America. There was then no Neotropical Region in the present sense. American camels, tapirs, and other animals now exclusively neotropical were pan-American in the Pleistocene and exclusively (in this hemisphere) North American before that. They are surely not neotropical in the historical sense, or in the same sense as, say, armadillos, which arose in South America and were until the late Tertiary confined to part of the Neotropical Region as now delimited.

In a historical view, then, the Neotropical Region ceases to be clear and consistent. Its fauna is not a coherent unit from this point of view, and its boundaries are not even approximately constant. In the historical study the static concept must be abandoned. The region and its fauna cannot be taken as either definite or invariable, but must be analyzed through a long series of shifts and fluxes.

## FAUNAL STRATA

In any given region, the various groups of animals will be found to have occupied that territory for different lengths of time. In general, the longer the group has been there, the more peculiar it will be to the local scene and the more strongly differentiated from relatives living elsewhere. The results of this process are particularly striking in South America. Armadillos and sloths belong to an order (Edentata) known nowhere else (aside from marginal spread into North America). Differentiation has proceeded so far in that region that there is now no clear trace of special relationship to animals of other regions, aside from the broadest fact that these edentates are placental mammals. The monkeys of South America are quite distinct, as a group, from those of the Old World and yet clearly related, belonging to the same order, Primates. They show an intermediate degree of regional differentiation. The field mice of South America, although distinctive as to species and, usually, genera, are closely related to those of North America, belonging not only to the same order (Rodentia) but also to the same family (Cricetidae) and even to the same subfamily and tribe. They have a low degree of regional differentiation.

The fossil record clearly confirms the fact that these varying degrees of differentiation are correlated with the time when the ancestors of these animals were emplaced in South America; edentates, high differentiation, in the earliest Cenozoic; primates, medium differentiation, in the mid-Cenozoic; cricetids, low differentiation, in the late Cenozoic. The three groups represent three readily distinguished faunal strata. The faunal history of South America has clearly been episodic.

The faunas of all regions are apparently stratified and their histories episodic in much this same way. On most continents, however, episodes of emplacement of new groups have been so frequent and so scattered in time, and their isolation from allied groups of other regions has been so imperfect, that the stratification is highly complex and the distinction of various strata is blurred. Only in South America and in the present island continent, Australia, are the strata relatively few in number and, as a rule, sharply and clearly separable. This clarity is a result of the physical history of the continent. Stratigraphic and paleontological evidence agree in clearly demonstrating that South America was isolated by sea barriers from all other continents from about the beginning of the Tertiary until near its end (probably early Paleocene to late Pliocene). During this long span, about 70 million years, its animals were genetically isolated from all other continental faunas, and therefore the introduction of new stocks was, although not completely prevented, extremely restricted.

Some complications exist in each case, but in broad lines the South American mammalian fauna can be analyzed into three strata. The oldest stratum, which may be called that of the "ancient immigrants," includes groups that reached South America before its complete isolation from the rest of the world, in latest Cretaceous or earliest Tertiary times, and the numerous and varied descendants of these ancient stocks. The second stratum, that of the "old island-hoppers," includes only two groups, old native rodents and monkeys, which reached South America while it was isolated. The third major stratum, of "late island-hoppers" and "late immigrants," with considerable complexity of detail, includes a great variety of animals that reached the continent in the late Tertiary and the Quaternary, shortly before and during its reconnection with North America. The three mammalian strata are shown in more detail in the table below, and their correlation with geographic events is diagrammatically suggested in Fig. 36.

For animals other than mammals, the fossil evidence is relatively poor. Most of the vertebrates have more or less clear indications of the same threefold stratification, with some probable blurring of the picture for groups less rigidly restricted by a sea barrier (such as some birds and probably some fishes). Among freshwater and terrestrial invertebrates, the fossil record of which is almost nil, there may be an added complication in the form of faunal strata still older than the oldest for mammals and most other vertebrates. On the whole, however, the three designated strata are pervasive in historical interpretation of the entire fauna.

## MAMMALIAN FAUNAL STRATIFICATION IN SOUTH AMERICA

| *Time of Emplacement* | *Faunal Stratum* | *Groups Introduced* | *Differentiation in South America* |
|---|---|---|---|
| Pliocene to Recent | III LATE (ISLAND-HOPPERS AND) IMMIGRANTS | Deer<br>Camels<br>Peccaries<br>Tapirs<br>Horses<br>Mastodons<br>Cats<br>Weasels<br>Raccoons<br>Bears<br>Dogs<br>Mice<br>Squirrels<br>Rabbits<br>Shrew | Already differentiated before emplacement in South America. Local differentiation of many genera, species, subspecies, no families or higher groups. |
| Late Eocene to Oligocene | II OLD ISLAND-HOPPERS | Protrogomorph rodents<br>Advanced lemuroids | Caviomorph rodents (many groups)<br>New World monkeys |
| Around earliest Paleocene | I ANCIENT IMMIGRANTS | Ferungulates (Condylarth-like complex) | Litopterns<br>Notoungulates (many groups)<br>Astrapotheres<br>Pyrotheres |
| | | Palaeanodonts — | Xenarthrans<br>Ground sloths<br>Tree sloths<br>Anteaters<br>Armadillos<br>Glyptodonts |
| | | Didelphoids — | (Didelphoids continued)<br>Borhyaenoids<br>Caenolestoids |

These faunal strata can be designated as such and thus dated only with respect to the geographic unit of South America and by virtue of its Tertiary isolation. In Central America, for instance, much the same groups of animals occur, but their time relationships and their associations in strata are quite different *with respect to the region occupied.* The oldest mammalian faunal strata in Central America include what are in South America the old island-hoppers and various of the late island-hoppers and immigrants. The old immigrants of South America, forming the *oldest* stratum there, belong to what is, generally speaking, the *youngest* stratum in Central America. There are profound differences in regional history in parts of what now is the broadly unified single Neotropical Region.

## THE PROBLEM OF BASIC MAMMALIAN FAUNAL TYPES

A fundamental problem regarding the Latin American mammalian fauna arises at the very beginning of its history. When the

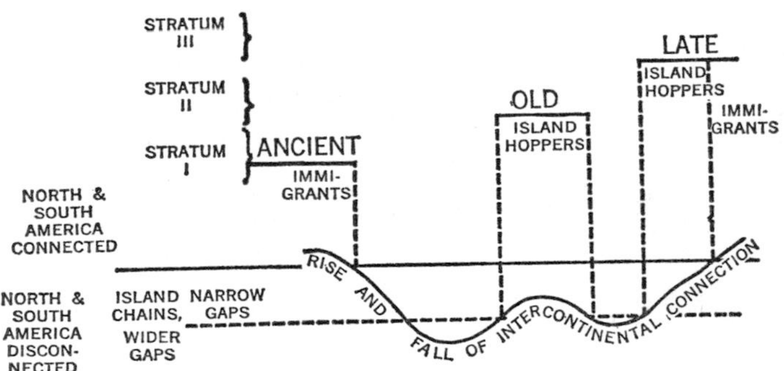


Fig. 36. Relationships between faunal strata in South America and the rise and fall of intercontinental land connections. The grasp is diagrammatic only, as the history of the connection was not so simple as shown, and the sea barriers shifted in position.

Age of Mammals began, with extinction of many groups of Mesozoic reptiles and the beginning of the rise of mammals to dominance in land faunas, the mammals were already, in fact, an old group. Although still small, obscure, and relatively unvaried, the major lines of mammals had then already split into two basically distinct divisions: marsupials and placentals or, technically, Metatheria and Eutheria.

Africa, Europe, Asia, and North America then formed an essentially continuous land mass, a World Continent. The continuity has been interrupted at various points from time to time and there have been innumerable faunal changes and marked regional differentiation in various groups, but the mammalian faunal type was then and remains today fundamentally the same throughout all parts of the World Continent. Marsupials were present at the start (at least in North America and Europe, and probably throughout), but they were of minor importance. The major ecological roles, and specifically those of carnivorous and herbivorous types, were played, as they still are, by placentals.

In Australia, probably then already an island continent (Notogaea), and in South America, then or shortly thereafter becoming an island continent (Neogaea), the basic faunal types with which the Age of Mammals began were radically different from the World Continent type. In Australia all the mammalian ecological roles were played by marsupials. (Such early faunas have not, in fact, been found in Australia, but this is a probable and generally accepted inference from the evidence of later faunas). In South America, the herbivores were mainly placentals, but the insectivorous, gnawing, and carnivorous types were marsupials.

Early attempts to explain this extraordinary anomaly between the South American island continent mammalian faunal type and the World Continent type usually involved the theory that South American marsupial carnivores were derived from Australia. (Why the carnivores of Australia were marsupials rather than placentals is another fundamental problem not here under consideration.) Among several serious objections to this idea is the extreme improbability that marsupial carnivores would spread from Australia to South America unaccompanied by their ecological associates and prey, the Australian marsupial herbivores. Other possible sources of mammalian faunas all had placental carnivores and placental herbivores, and equal difficulty is encountered in explaining the spread to South America of these herbivores without their associates, the placental carnivores. That the carnivorous and herbivorous elements in the first, balanced, basic South American mammalian fauna should each have come separately and from a totally distinct source is simply incredible.

An alternative view is that the basic South American fauna did have an essentially unified geographic origin, all coming from (or at any rate being connected with) the World Continent fauna. In that case, however, it might appear that placental carnivores must have been included but must almost immediately have become extinct in South America. Such extinction has been considered inherently improbable, because in the established cases of competition between marsupial and placental carnivores, the placentals have survived and the marsupials have become extinct. The placental dingo survived in Australia and its marsupial analogue, the thylacine, became extinct (except on the separate island of Tasmania which was not reached by the dingo). The last South American marsupial carnivores disappeared as placental carnivores (of the latest major faunal stratum) arrived. It is an additional difficulty that specialized marsupial carnivores are quite unknown from any age on the World Continent and probably never occurred there. Similarly, placental carnivores are totally unknown in the early South American faunas, and extinction so rapid and complete as to eliminate all traces in the now rather abundant Tertiary fossil collections seems improbable, although not impossible.

These objections largely disappear, and a reasonable solution of this long-disputed problem can be suggested, if one gives consideration to the relatively undifferentiated and primitive mammals of the earliest Tertiary, rather than thinking in terms of the more familiar, sharply distinct, and specialized later forms. The basic World Continent fauna, at its very beginning, did not include radically differentiated placental carnivores and herbivores. These two later ecological types were then ancestrally represented by one basic stock, to which I have elsewhere applied the name "ferungulate." This stock was rapidly becoming considerably varied and apparently included some rather more herbivorous and some rather more carnivorous forms, but as a whole it was omnivorous and all its members were still closely similar. Among the fossils of this group, some are classified as Carnivora and some as Condylarthra (primitive ungulates), because of our knowledge of the *subsequent* sharp ordinal distinctions of their descendants. If we did not know their later history, the early forms would certainly be placed in the same order and very likely in the same family or even smaller group.

It was this more generalized ferungulate stock, and not any later and then truly distinctive placental carnivores and herbivores, that figured in the beginnings of the oldest faunal stratum of South America. On the World Continent this stock was associated with likewise primitive marsupials, which also lacked as yet any distinctive specializations as carnivores but were equally capable (as the event proved) of such a development. In the World Continent, *after* it was cut off from South America, specialized carnivores arose among the ferungulate lines, and their occupation of this ecological specialty impeded the rise there of marsupial carnivores. In South America, likewise after separation from the World Continent, marsupials more rapidly developed carnivorous types. This in itself would tend sufficiently to inhibit the rise there of placental carnivores among the ferungulates, which rapidly developed a great variety of types all more or less herbivorous.

Thus there was no competition between marsupial carnivores and placental carnivores, as such, and probably only marginal competition between marsupials and placentals as a whole, but only a parceling out of the various ecological zones, which happened to receive different occupants in the World Continent and in South America. Why the ferungulates evolved more rapidly into specialized carnivores on the World Continent and the marsupials (didelphoids) in South America is not evident. It is, nevertheless, plausible that this could occur, and the hypothesis that it did occur seems to be the only one that reasonably accounts for these differences in basic faunal type.

There may be some remaining objection that placentals in general are superior to marsupials and would tend, in South America or elsewhere, to occupy any and all ecological niches, including those of carnivores, at the expense of the marsupials. This possible objection really has little or no force. Present evidence is that the placentals are not more advanced derivatives from backward or older marsupials, as was commonly believed in the 19th century and is still occasionally stated in textbooks. Placentals and marsupials seem rather to represent a basic dichotomy of the main mammalian stock and to have been about equally progressive and adaptively efficient when they arose. Primitive forms of the two major branches apparently lived together in ecological equilibrium, and even today the opossums of North and South America remain abundant and are eminently successful in holding their own in the midst of the dominant placental faunas. Ecological incompatibility between marsupials and placentals seems to arise only when late and narrowly specialized forms come in contact within essentially the same ecological niche, a situation in which *any* two groups, and not only marsupials and placentals, become ecologically incompatible. Even on this score, the extinction of South American and Australian marsupial carnivores in competition with placental carnivores gives evidence not particularly that placentals are superior to marsupials but that the late World Continent groups had become competitively superior to those of the island continents. In South America, the old native placental groups were also decimated when they came into contact with placentals from the World Continent. They fared no better than the marsupials of similar geographic history.

## ORIGINS OF THE OLDEST FAUNAL ELEMENTS

Probably the most disputed single question of Latin American zoogeography has been the geographic origin or, at least, connections of the older faunal elements. The principal question raised has concerned possible direct relationships among the southern continents, between South America and Australia, on one side, or Africa, on the other. The various postulates include transoceanic land bridges or continents, land connections by way of Antarctica, or early continental union followed by fracturing and drift (Wegenerian) to the present widely separated positions of the three continents. A summary of the truly voluminous and polemic literature of this subject is outside the scope of the present study, but the nature of the older mammalian faunas and the evidence these give as to their origin will be briefly reviewed.

The major elements among the mammalian old immigrants and their possible origins are as follows (see also Figs. 37 and 38).

*Marsupials.* These were already quite varied in the older Tertiary, with primitive, more or less insectivorous types, rodentlike types, and marsupial carnivores. A possible common origin of all would be in a varied assemblage of relatively unspecialized marsupials, didelphoid or extremely primitive dasyuroid in general character. Such an assemblage is known from the late Cretaceous of North America, where primitive marsupials (opossums) also occurred through the Paleocene and later. Similar forms occur doubtfully in the Paleocene and surely in the Eocene of Europe. Elsewhere the evidence is purely negative.

*Edentates.* The oldest South American faunas include only armadillos, of primitive type, among edentates. The other groups appear, evidently by evolution within the continent, during the early and middle Tertiary: glyptodonts and ground sloths by late Eocene, anteaters in the Miocene, tree sloths (with practically no established fossil record) by rather minor differentiation from the less specialized ground sloths some time around the mid-Tertiary. The only firmly established special relationships with any non-South American mammals are with the Palaeanodonta, a group more primitive in general character than any of the South American edentates and known only from North America (late Paleocene to middle Eocene, with a probable more specialized offshoot in the early Oligocene).

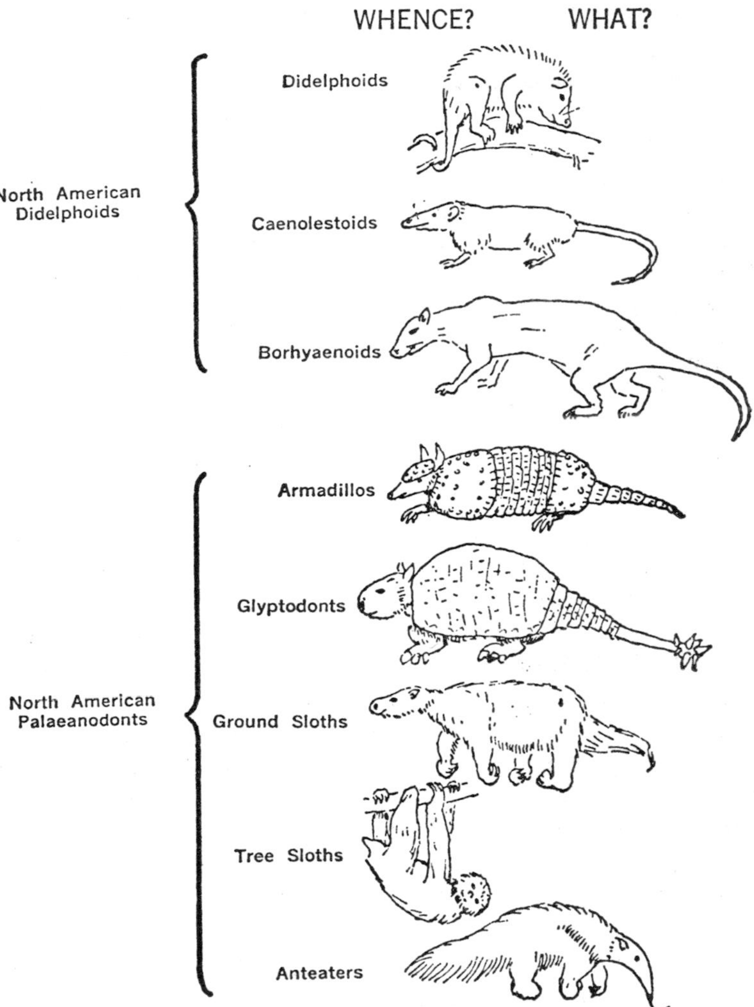


Fig. 37. Marsupials and edentates, evolved in the oldest mammalian faunal stratum of South America, and their possible origins. (Not drawn to scale.)

*Condylarths*. These most primitive of ungulate herbivores were fairly common in the Paleocene-Eocene faunas of South America and some lingered on into the Oligocene (or possibly the Miocene). The same order was important in the basic World Continent fauna. It occurs abundantly throughout the Paleocene and Eocene of North America, and some North and South American genera are suggestive of special relationship.

*Litopterns*. This order, known only from South America, was common and varied in early faunas and persisted, in decreasing variety, into the Pleistocene. Early forms are near the condylarths, to such an extent that the litopterns might be considered merely as surviving and diversely specialized condylarths. They seem to have originated in South America from the South American condylarths, and therefore to have the same source as the latter.

*Notoungulates*. This great order of hoofed herbivores constitutes the bulk of earlier South American faunas and continues, with radically decreasing variety, into the Pleistocene. It suggests a group similar in origin and parallel in history to the litopterns. An odd anomaly arises from the discovery of a notoungulate in the late Paleocene of Asia and a related form in the early Eocene of North America, the only occurrences of the order outside of South America. Origin in Asia and migration to South America by way of North America are suggested by the face of these facts, and this remains a possibility but is rendered rather improbable by various considerations. Early Eocene is too late a time for entry into South America. The most primitive South American forms are slightly but definitely less specialized than those known from Asia and North America. Another possibility is that the latter were strays *from* South America. The question cannot now be resolved, but a faunal connection of one sort or another is indicated with the northern continents.

*Astrapotheres*. Although never highly varied, these aberrant hoofed herbivores appeared early in South America and persisted into the Miocene. They probably arose in that continent and have no evident close or special relationships with other known groups, except that they probably originated ultimately from condylarths

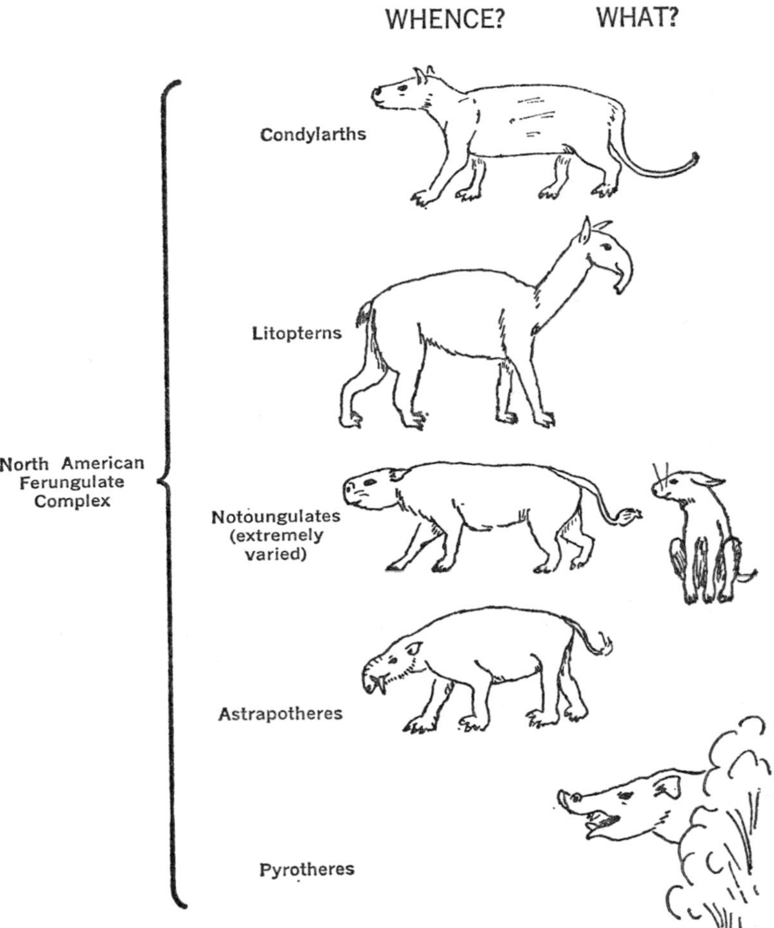


Fig. 38. Ungulates of the oldest mammalian faunal stratum of South America, and their possible origins. (Not drawn to scale.)

or primitive ferungulates in a broader sense. They could have some collateral relationship or, at least, functional parallelism with archaic World Continent forms like the pantodonts and uintatheres, known in particular abundance from North America but also spreading to Eurasia.

*Pyrotheres.* These odd, superficially mastodon-like ungulates were never much varied or particularly common, as far as known, but they appear in early Eocene faunas and persist into the Oligocene. They are known only from South America and probably arose in that continent. Special relationships are not known, but in broad terms differentiation from the basic ferungulate complex is indicated, more or less as for the astrapotheres. True relationship to the Proboscidea has been suggested, but now seems untenable except as the Proboscidea may also represent a separate branch from a part (paenungulate) of the ferungulate complex.

Recent work by C. de Paula Conto on early mammals from Brazil has greatly increased knowledge of ancient South American mammals and has also added definite recognition of an order of ungulates, Xenungulata, additional to those noted above. These discoveries tend to increase known resemblances to North American faunas and to support the following conclusions.

The data on the very earliest Tertiary mammals of South America and of the world as a whole are so scanty that tracing of exact lineages cannot be expected and is not, in fact, possible at present. In broad terms, this assemblage certainly suggests derivation from the World Continent fauna and *could not* be derived from Australia unless it is assumed, quite gratuitously and contrary to such evidence (all indirect) as exists, that Australia did once have a basic fauna of World Continent type and later eliminated almost the whole of this fauna. Within the World Continent, there is absolutely no evidence of any special relationship of Africa with South America. This is partly a negative conclusion, because Paleocene mammals are unknown from Africa, but it would, again, be wholly gratuitous to assume that relationships existed and left no trace in the late Eocene and subsequent African faunas.

Such definite evidence of relationships as exists all points most nearly to North America. Every South American stock is related at least as closely to one known from North America as to any other known group outside of South America, and the edentates have no established relationships except with an exclusively North American group. In view of these relationships and of the fact that South America is now geographically closest to North America (and nothing impels the belief that this was untrue at the end of the Cretaceous), the tendency of so many students to look elsewhere for the main geographic relationships of the old South American fauna almost smacks of a preference for the unlikely over the obvious.

The question remains whether the World Continent fauna might not have been derived from South America, as the great Argentine student, Ameghino, insisted, rather than the other way around. In the exact sense of Ameghino, who believed that later specialized orders and families originated in South America and spread hence over the rest of the world, this certainly is not true. In the sense that some elements of the most basic World Continent fauna might have become differentiated in South America while that continent was united to North America and hence in a sense part of the World Continent, the possibility remains but it seems quite improbable. The old South American faunas seem to represent diversification on that continent from a sampling of the World Continent fauna that was partial only (no insectivores, no early primates, no early rodents, no differentiated creodonts, only highly aberrant paenungulates). No forms conceivably near the ancestry of any World Continent lineages have ever actually been found in the old South American faunas.

Clearly inconclusive, the evidence does suggest North America as the probable source of the old South American fauna. It does not completely exclude, but definitely does not support, other possibilities. This conclusion finds further, indirect but strong, substantiation from the evidence that South America was connected with North America toward the end of the Age of Reptiles. Although opposite statements may still be found in the literature, it is at present recognized by the most competent specialists on these faunas

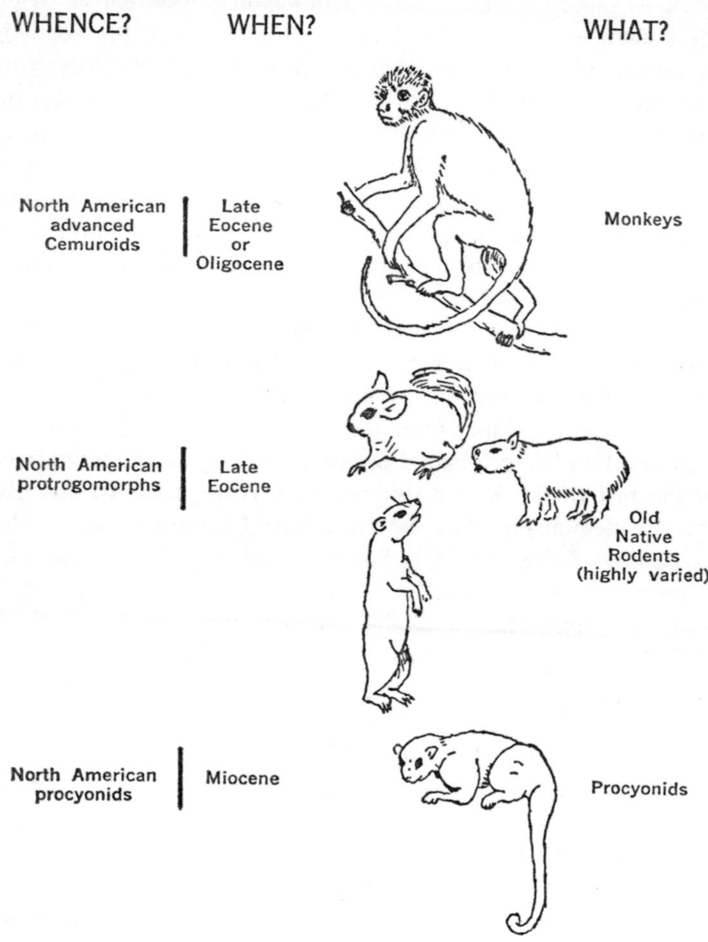


Fig. 39. Derivatives of island-hopping immigrants into South America, and their probable origins. The monkeys and old native rodents form the second or intermediate mammalian faunal stratum. The procyonids (allies of the raccoon) may be considered rather as forerunners of the last, relatively complex, faunal stratum. (Not drawn to scale.)

that the late Cretaceous reptiles of South America are, as a group, more like those of North America than like any known faunas elsewhere in the world.

## THE OLD ISLAND-HOPPERS

The origin of the second faunal stratum of South America, although less discussed as a separate problem, has been in many ways even more puzzling. This stratum comprises the old native rodents, which are the so-called South American hystricomorphs, and the neotropical primates. (See Fig. 39.) These rodents first appear in the record in beds somewhat uncertainly correlated as early Oligocene, and primates are first known from later beds, considered with similar uncertainty as late Oligocene. Both occurrences are marginal on the continent (in Patagonia) and do not exclude the possibility that the groups had been for some time in more central or northern parts of the continent, where adequate faunas of appropriate age have not been discovered. It is, however, improbable that emplacement of these groups in South America was long prior to the Oligocene and it seems almost certain that their ancestors were not among the early immigrants. There is no evidence that entry of the two groups was absolutely simultaneous, and, indeed, it probably was not. Both, however, entered South America at about the same time, roughly midway between the two major immigrations; the two have become comparably differentiated there, and it is justified to consider them broadly as of the same faunal stratum.

Both these groups have repeatedly been cited as indicating faunal relationships with Africa. The neotropical monkeys, although distinctly definable as a group, resemble the Old World (including African) monkeys and are on a similar evolutionary level. The old South American rodents also show resemblances to some Old World rodents (porcupines figure in both regions, for instance), and among them are some, in the general group of the hutias, degus, tucutucus, and spiny "rats" (not true rats), that particularly resemble some African rodents, the cane and rock "rats" (also not true rats).

Recent studies seem rather conclusively to controvert these apparent African affinities. The South American primates, including the earliest forms, are in some respects more primitive than the Old World forms of similar or later age and in some respects differently specialized. The former characters seem to prohibit derivation of the New from the Old World forms, and the latter seem to exclude filiation in the other direction. There is a strong suggestion that the New and Old World monkeys represent geographically separated parallel developments from a more remote and primitive (technically prosimian) ancestry. Many years ago, the late J. W. Gidley suggested that neotropical monkeys might be derived from a group of prosimians (Notharctinae) relatively abundant in the Eocene of North America, and the Old World monkeys from Old World allies of this group. Too little attention has been given to this suggestion, but recent study is adding some evidence in its favor and it is now the best working hypothesis as regards the New World forms, at least.

It had been suspected from time to time that the history of the New and Old World "hystricomorph" rodents might be a similar case of independent, parallel development from allied New and Old World groups of primitive Eocene rodents, but concrete evidence has been scanty. More recently (in 1949), in describing relatively complete material of the oldest and most primitive known South American rodent, A. E. Wood has found positive evidence for their derivation not from a distinct hystricomorph stock but from a widespread World Continent group of most primitive rodents (Ischyromyidae, *sensu lato*). Among these, he finds particular resemblance to some North American forms (especially the mid-Eocene *Reithroparamys*).

There is, then, good reason to believe that the idea of special African relationships for these groups, old South American rodents and monkeys, is incorrect and that both are of North American origin. The evidence is, indeed, better than for the older immigrants, for in each case a possible North American ancestry can be rather closely designated among well-known groups.

It seems quite clear that these groups did not follow a land bridge from North America. When they entered South America, North America was swarming with rapidly progressive mammals of other types, notably many placental carnivores and a variety of perissodactyl and artiodactyl ungulates. It is incredible that an open migration route existed without any effect other than spread southward of just two stocks, possibly only a single introduction in each case. Entry was almost certainly by waif dispersal over what I have called a "sweepstakes route." Both groups, initially small and probably arboreal animals, are ecological types especially apt for such dispersal. Geological evidence in Central America and northwestern South America perfectly fits this picture. During late Eocene and Oligocene, the pertinent times in this connection, there was clearly a series of seaways between North and South America, interrupted by a series of islands. The seaways would bar any extensive faunal interchange. The islands would facilitate overseas spread of a few special groups, literally island-hoppers. Although it would, of course, be possible to postulate a similar island chain elsewhere, to Africa, for instance, no evidence known to me really suggests this, and the postulate is unnecessary and unsupported.

The immediate source of the immigrants would, of course, be Middle America or what is now tropical North America, and not the region from New Mexico to Montana where early Tertiary faunas are now known. Transition from the archaic ancestral groups (prosimians for the monkeys and protogomorphs [of Wood] for the rodents) to the characteristic Latin American groups (ceboids and "hystricomorphs" or, perhaps better, caviomorphs, respectively) doubtless occurred in the paleontological *terra incognita* of early Middle America. Some basic diversification of these groups may also have occurred in Middle America and have been under way even before they island-hopped to the southern continent.

## DEVELOPMENT OF THE NATIVE FAUNA

The oldest reasonably well-known South American mammalian faunas (Eocene of Patagonia) are dominated by the typical and highly varied native ungulate herbivores of the Order Notoungulata, which includes nearly half of the known genera of that time. The rest of the known fauna is divided about equally among condylarths, litopterns, edentates, and marsupials (groups characterized on previous pages). Pyrotheres and astrapotheres were present and are striking animals, but were quite minor elements in the total fauna. One other paenungulate order was also present then or still earlier, but was also a very minor element of the whole fauna (de Paula Conto). It soon disappeared.

Until the late Pliocene, the faunal composition changed rather steadily but with few really profound modifications. The condylarths dwindled and finally became extinct, with ecological replacement by their collateral descendants, the litopterns. The notoungulates, exuberantly varied in the Eocene, continued in force but show a steady decrease in variety as primitive and intermediate lines were weeded out and a smaller number of more sharply distinct and specialized lines continued. On the other hand, the edentates, relatively little varied in the Eocene, expanded steadily into the Miocene when, in variety of genera, they constituted about a third of the known faunas. Pyrotheres and astrapotheres died out, the former in the Oligocene and the latter by the end of the Miocene.

The most noteworthy change before the late Pliocene followed the appearance of the second faunal stratum, that of the old island-hoppers. The old native rodents expanded steadily and greatly into the Pliocene, where they include about a third of the known mammalian genera. Similar, but less intense, expansion of the primates may be postulated, although they are absent in most of the known fossil deposits, which generally represent facies unsuitable for this predominantly tropical and arboreal group. The broader lines of this long faunal development are seen in Fig. 40.

The greatest interest of the phase of South American faunal history while the continent was an island lies in the fact that it is a sort of large-scale natural experiment in evolution. The old immigrants rapidly occupied the large and varied continent, and the faunas then evolved there in dynamic equilibrium, undisturbed by wider genetic interchange or by irruptions from without other than those of the old island-hoppers—and this exception is itself so relatively simple and analyzable that it almost ideally exemplifies the process and consequences of single major additions to an evolving fauna.

The first striking evolutionary phenomena illustrated are those of "explosive" or "eruptive" evolution and adaptive radiation. The poorly known Paleocene faunas and, particularly, the better known early Eocene faunas are at a most active stage of this process. Everything here indicates the culmination of an exceptionally rapid and burgeoning expansion of the mammalian fauna into a great variety of ecological niches which were, before this episode, empty or nearly so. The number of separate groups, from generic to family levels, at least, is exceptionally large. Intergradation between lines later widely distinct is still common. There seems to be considerable overlapping and even duplication in ecological types within the same or adjacent local faunas. Variation within specific populations is often exceptionally great, a basis for rapid diversifi-

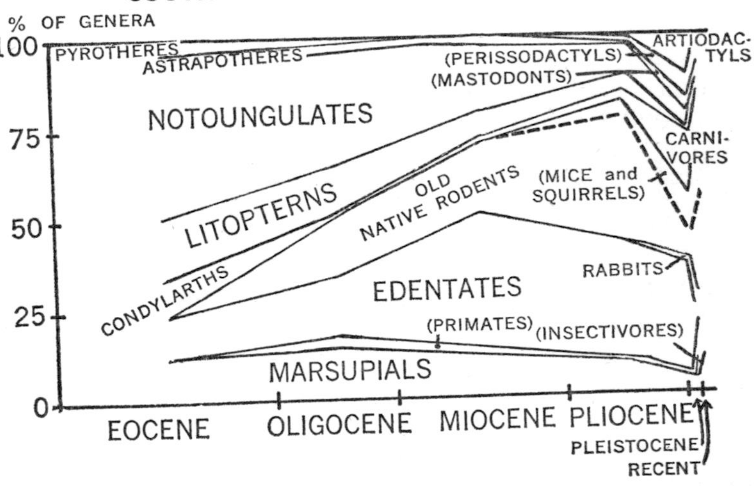


Fig. 40. Development of the land mammals of South America. For each epoch the composition of the fauna is shown in terms of percentage of known genera belonging to the various orders of mammals.

cation speciational in pattern, and an indication that marked segregation of characters and specialization of adaptive type are under way but still incomplete.

Disappearance of intermediate types and fixation of a smaller number of well-defined groups each with a characteristic, separate, and progressively specialized adaptive and ecological status were processes evident through the later Eocene and Oligocene. This process was essentially completed in the Miocene as far as the descendants of most of the ancient immigrants are concerned, although the old native rodents and some of the edentates were then still in an expanding phase. The result of the process is a sort of parceling out of the available ways of life among the various stocks of mammals, an adaptive radiation.

In the meantime, on the World Continent even more varied ways of life were being occupied by adaptive radiation, or a more complex, interlocking series of over-all and local adaptive radiations, going on without contact with the South American fauna. When World Continent and South American lines became specialized for similar ecological roles, they also came to resemble each other functionally and morphologically. Parallel and convergent evolution was thus illustrated on a large scale. Another independent radiation in Australia produced another set of parallel and convergent types. Sometimes the separate lines departed from the same more or less remote common ancestry and evolved in close parallel, as in the case of the carnivorous marsupials of South America and of Australia. This process produces closest resemblance, a fact responsible for long debate on the affinities of these marsupial carnivores and for former insistence on the part of some students that South America and Australia must somehow have shared advanced and specialized marsupials and not merely the remote and primitive ancestors of these.

In other cases quite different groups have evolved toward similar adaptive types, a process producing less complete, convergent resemblance, as between the marsupial carnivores and the World Continent's placental carnivores. The two processes of parallelism and convergence intergrade and cannot be sharply defined in given

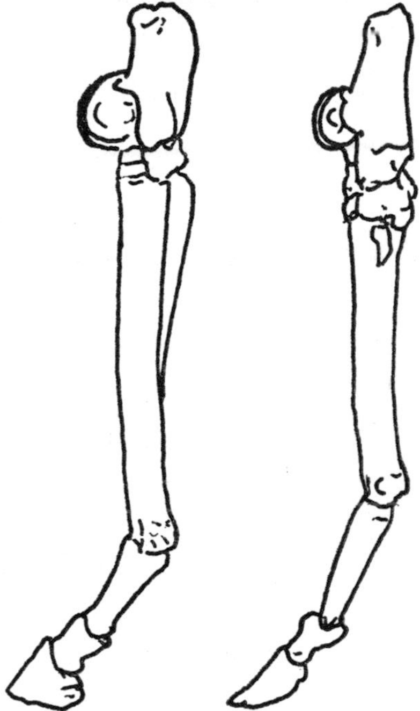

Fig. 41. Side views of hind feet of the modern horse, *Equus* (*left*), and of an extinct South American pseudo-horse, the litoptern *Thoatherium* (*right*), to show convergence in foot structure of these two one-toed mammals. Note vestiges of side toes, larger in the true horse than in this pseudo-horse. (Not drawn to scale; *Equus* is larger than *Thoatherium*.) Redrawn after W. D. Matthew.

cases. The striking similarity of some North American horses and some South American litopterns, evolving independently from a more or less remote condylarth ancestry, is a case in point. It can be interpreted either as straight parallelism from the common ancestral and condylarth stage or as divergence, origin of the different orders Perissodactyla and Litopterna, followed by convergence between lineages in two families of these orders, Equidae in the first and Proterotheriidae in the second.

The faunas well illustrate the limitations of these processes, which produce similarities of various degrees but apparently never, even in cases of close parallelism, produce real identity, in part or in whole. In the flesh, a superficial or distant observer might well have confused *Diadiaphorus,* a South American litoptern, with *Miohippus,* a North American horse, but no competent anatomist would mistake any tooth or bone of one for the other.

Another interesting point is that such developments were not necessarily synchronous in the two cases. *Thoatherium,* a litoptern, was completely one-toed in the early Miocene. Horses did not become one-toed until the Pliocene, and even today *Equus* is less advanced than *Thoatherium* was in this respect. (See Fig. 41.) Some lines of notoungulates in South America had very high-crowned, complexly crested, cement-covered grazing teeth in the early Oligocene; horses did not reach a comparable stage until the late Miocene. These examples illustrate, by the way, that South American animals were not altogether less progressive or more slowly evolving than those of the World Continent, as has sometimes been supposed.

In many cases convergence was quite incomplete or would involve only a particular functional resemblance and not a close equivalence of total ecological status. Glyptodonts, for instance, the rigidly bulky cousins of the armadillo, seem to have been grazing forms and so have this functional resemblance with various ungulate grazers, but even their teeth are built on a plan wholly different from that of any ungulate. The glyptodonts as a whole can hardly be compared with any ungulate, or indeed with any World Continent animals. Such forms as some litopterns and some horses may be considered ecological vicars in their respective areas, but others, like the glyptodonts, are ecological uniques.

## LATE FAUNAL MIXTURE AND ITS OUTCOME

In the World Continent, there was a radical turnover in faunal type rather early in the Tertiary, mainly during the Eocene. In terms, for instance, of percentage composition of the mammalian faunas by orders or suborders, the difference between a Paleocene and an Oligocene fauna in North America is striking and almost absolute. Changes in this respect, of broad lines of faunal composition, have been relatively slight since the Oligocene. The modern faunal type was beginning to appear and to replace the oldest type even in the Eocene, thus here aptly called "Dawn of the Recent." Not so, however, in South America. There, as we have already seen in passing, change was gradual and involved no really fundamental upset of faunal type into the Pliocene. The mid-Pliocene fauna, in most of its broadest features, was not radically unlike a Paleocene fauna in spite of very pronounced advancing specialization in most of the orders and the Oligocene insertion into the fauna of two new orders (Primates, Rodentia).

A change like that going on in the Eocene on the World Continent also occurred in South America, but at a greatly later date, in the late Pliocene and Pleistocene (Fig. 40). Its cause was the rise of the Central American bridge and the consequent irruption into South America of many derivatives from the fauna of the World Continent. This third broad faunal stratum did not come in all at once, in a single wave. Perhaps in the early Pliocene a few northern forms appeared, small arboreal placental carnivores more or less related to the raccoon. Not long thereafter, at least by middle Pliocene times, some South American animals, ground sloths, reached North America. These forerunners do not seem to indicate a continuous land connection but probably utilized the island chain, gaps in which were closing progressively as the Central American and northwestern South American regions rose relative to sea level. The exact moment when the bridge became complete is not established, but this probably occurred during the age called Chapadmalalan in South America and Blancan in North America, placed by some authorities as latest Pliocene and by others as earliest Pleistocene. Even then the exchange was at first rather limited in scope, and the full surge of intermigration did not occur until somewhat later, in unequivocally Pleistocene times. Soon or late, at least 15 (possibly 16) families invaded South America in this great episode. (See Fig. 42.)

Invasion occurred in both directions. By a moderate tabulation, 15 families of North American mammals then spread into South America and 7 families spread in the reverse direction. The main migrants to the south were rabbits, squirrels, field mice, dogs, bears, raccoons, weasels, cats, mastodons, horses, tapirs, peccaries, camels, and deer, including in most of these cases some variety of related forms.

The immediate effect was to produce in both continents, but particularly in South America, a greatly enriched fauna. To a fauna already large and essentially complete or closed ecologically were added a large number of new forms from the other continent. The enrichment inevitably involved some duplication. No two forms of different origin can have been precisely and fully equal in their needs and capacities, but many were sufficiently similar to be in competition for food and, in general, living space. Some native groups held their own and some invading groups became extinct, but some native groups disappeared and (as a rule) were replaced by invaders.

In the end—that is, at the present time—South America has returned to about the same basic richness of fauna as before the invasion. Recent families of mammals there number the same (more or less, depending on the classification used) as in the Pliocene before invasion, but the faunal composition is radically different. The notoungulates, litopterns, and marsupial carnivores have entirely disappeared. The native rodents and edentates are greatly reduced. In their places, artiodactyls, perissodactyls, rodents of northern origin (squirrels, cricetids), rabbits, and placental carnivores are fully entrenched and constitute, in number of genera, about half of the recent fauna.

The main determinants in this process were, first, ecological status and, second, place of origin. Ecological uniques tended to survive (Fig. 43). It is true that glyptodonts and ground sloths, after

Fig. 42. Representatives of the principal families of previously North American mammals that invaded South America late in the Cenozoic, and which form the youngest mammalian faunal stratum there. (Not drawn to scale.)

spreading over both continents, became extinct and that they apparently were ecological uniques. The question of their extinction involves some other and not properly understood factor, and it is

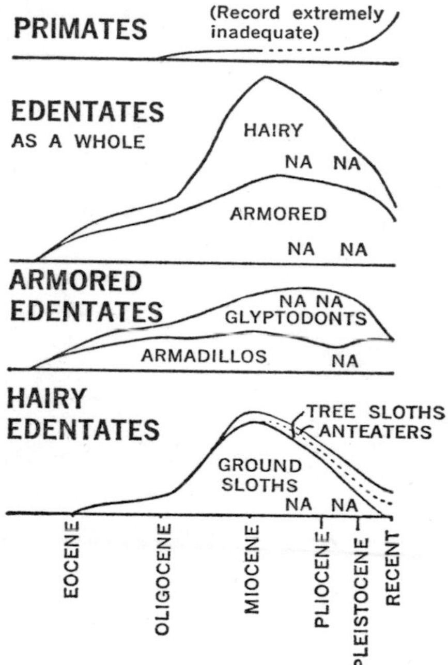


Fig. 43. Development of some South American groups that were ecologically unique with respect to late invaders from North America. Height of the graph in each case represents the relative number of known genera. The time scale at the bottom applies to all graphs. NA = migration to North America. (Some of the old native rodents were also ecologically unique; see Fig. 44.)

part of a larger question that cannot be discussed here. The smaller, likewise or even more strictly ecologically unique, relatives of these animals—armadillos, tree sloths, and anteaters—did survive. So did the monkeys, ecological uniques with respect to North America, and most of the truly ecologically unique old native rodents.

When ecological vicars met, one or the other generally became extinct (Fig. 55). In South America, old native ungulates disappeared and ungulates of northern origin survived. Many old native rodents (about half the generic lines) became extinct and rabbits, squirrels, and field mice survived. Marsupial carnivores became extinct and placental carnivores survived. The fact that in each case the survivors were of northern origin cannot be pure coincidence. It is not explanatory to say that the animals from North America were "superior" or "more progressive," and such statements would be hard to substantiate by any objective evidence from their anatomy, for instance.

The ultimate factors have not been, and probably cannot be, designated, but a generalized explanation presents itself. North American animals had intermittently throughout the Age of Mammals and almost continuously in its later part been involved in the flux and intermigration of the World Continent. Those extant in the Plio-Pleistocene were the ones that had been successful in a long series of competitive episodes. They were specialists in invasion and in meeting competitive invaders. South American mammals had competed among themselves in the early Tertiary, but by about the end of the Oligocene they had essentially completed a process of parceling out the ecological opportunities among a number of practically noncompeting lines. Thereafter until the late Pliocene they met no impact from outside their own closed economy, and when it came, they had not evolved the required defenses.

Thus the recent South American mammalian fauna is a complex agglomeration, in spite of the fact that processes of ecological adjustment have again reduced it to an essentially balanced economy. It may all be ultimately derived from North America, and some of the evidence to that effect has been summarized. This evidence is suggestive but inconclusive for the oldest elements,

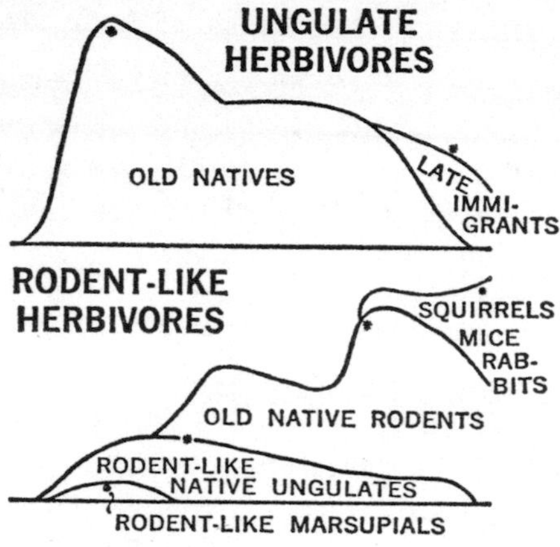


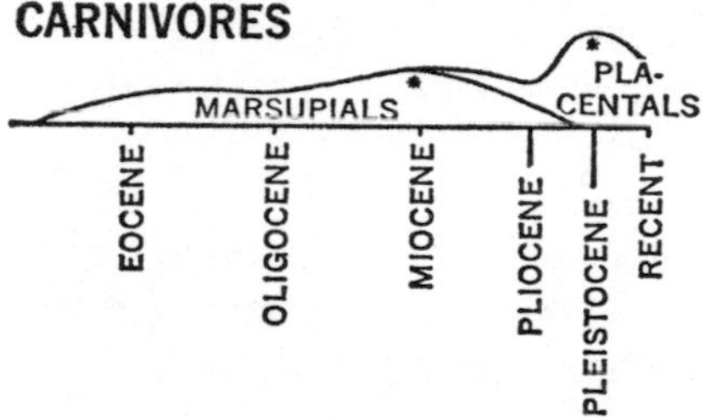


Fig. 44. Development in South America of ecological vicars, similar in adaptation to invading types from North America. Height of the graph in each case represents the relative number of known genera. The time scale at the bottom applies to all graphs. Top and bottom graphs show simple, total replacement of old groups by late invaders from North America. The more complex middle graph shows total replacement of old rodentlike marsupials (Polydolopidae) by other old native rodentlike forms, partial replacement of old rodentlike ungulates (mainly typotheres and hegetotheres) by old native true rodents, and then partial replacement of most of the latter by rabbits and true rodents in the late invasion from North America. Surviving old native rodents are, in the main, ecologically unique, with no closely similar competitors among the late invaders.

* = apogee.

stronger for the mid-Cenozoic elements, and conclusive and unquestioned for the latest elements. Even if all did have the same geographic origin, there are the three quite distinct broad faunal strata. Their different times of entry into South America complicate the picture, not only because of corresponding differences in differentiation within that continent but also because each stratum was drawn from a different sort of World Continent fauna. Differentiation, replacement, intermigration, complex stratification, divergent specialization, and other processes were constantly going on in the World Continent, and the strata of South American mammals sampled this sequence at three very different levels.

The static zoogeographic picture in a classical sense, of current resemblances and differences of regional faunas, is further complicated by differential regional extinction. Pumas link North and South America in nonhistorical zoogeography because they now occur on both continents, and camels separate the faunal regions, because they occur in South but not in North America. But in the Pleistocene pumas and camels occurred throughout both continents and in the Pliocene their ancestors were present in North but not in South America. Final analysis of the existing relationships of South and North American faunas must involve this factor together with the factor of stratification.

In the table below an attempt is made to analyze the now extant South American mammals with respect to their geographic history and their present relationships to mammals in the recent North American fauna (north of the tropical zone).

## ANALYSIS OF ZOOGEOGRAPHIC RELATIONSHIPS OF SOUTH AMERICAN RECENT MAMMALS, WITH RESPECT TO NORTH AMERICA

- I. Oldest South American faunal stratum, from North America (?) in late Cretaceous-Paleocene.
  - A. Collaterals (strongly differentiated) from same level present in North America.
    - 1. Without late level spread and recent presence in North America: caenolestids (North American collaterals:

opossums). (Some students would place the caenolestids under $IB_1$ and the opossums under $IB_2$; this may be correct but seems unlikely at present.)

2. With late level spread, etc.: none.

B. Ancient stock extinct in North America.

1. Without late level spread and recent presence in North America: none.
2. With late level spread, etc.: armadillos (N. A. distribution restricted).

II. Intermediate South American faunal stratum, from North America in Oligocene.

A. Collaterals (well differentiated) from same level present in N. A.

1. Without late level spread, etc.: "hystricomorphs" or caviomorphs except porcupines (differentiated N. A. collaterals: sewellel, squirrels, etc.).
2. With late level spread, etc.: porcupines.

B. Ancient stock extinct in North America.

1. Without late level spread, etc.: monkeys. (No collaterals in N. A. wild fauna, but man could be considered as such.)
2. With late level spread, etc.: none.

III. Late South American faunal stratum, from North America in late Pliocene and Quaternary.

A. Collaterals from same level (here poorly differentiated and representing essentially the same immediate stock) present in N. A. Late level spread back to N. A. possible in some cases, but in that event part of the same general episode of intermigration as emplacement of the South American stratum: opossums (history somewhat questionable, sometimes considered $IB_2$, but probably belonging here), shrews (marginal and with slight penetration in S. A.), rabbits, squirrels, cricetids, dogs, bears, raccoons, weasels, cats, peccaries (marginal and with slight penetration in N. A.), deer.

B. Collaterals extinct in N. A.: tapirs, camels. (Peccaries, listed under A, are marginal between A and B.)

This analysis is on a family level. More refined analysis, to genera or below, would involve some changes of status in the last stratum.

Central America, with its peculiar faunal history and its intermediate faunal types, is not involved in this comparison, which is based on the fully South American and the temperate-zone North American faunas. Special consideration of Central America is now necessary.

## THE ROLE OF CENTRAL AMERICA

There is and doubtless always has been considerable difference between regional faunas within South America. The faunas of the Patagonian pampas, the Andine punas, and the tropical rain forests are strikingly distinct. They are, nevertheless, regional varieties or differentiates of a general South American fauna and they share much the same sort of differences from and resemblances to the general fauna of temperate North America. There have not, during the Cenozoic, been any absolute barriers between regions within South America, and no outstanding effects of isolation are historically evident in separate parts of the continent. At most there has been a sort of climatic zoning by which animals once more widespread have become confined to particular, areally definable environments (primates to tropical forests, camels to mountains and cold plains, etc.), or the faunas of deteriorating environments have been progressively impoverished (in Patagonia, for example). Mid-Cenozoic faunas lately found in Colombia (co-operatively by the Colombian government and the University of California, under the direction of R. A. Stirton) have interesting regional differences from contemporaneous Patagonian faunas, but are definitely of the same general type and reveal no unexpectedly exotic groups. An old idea that northern and southern South America were separated by a Tertiary sea barrier and had quite distinct faunal histories, an idea still current among a few students but long rejected by others, is thus conclusively proved false.

There are, nevertheless, two regions of (broadly speaking) Latin America and of the Neotropical Region of static zoogeography that have had faunal histories decidedly different from that of

South America: Central, or in a somewhat broader sense Middle, America and the West Indies. The development of the West Indian fauna is one of the most fascinating topics of historical zoogeography and has been the subject of long, sometimes bitterly polemic discussion involving fundamental principles of this science. It is, however, of minor importance for the present broader theme and cannot be considered here. The West Indies have been a faunal dead end. There is little evidence that they have had a reciprocal influence on the larger faunas of the continental mainlands.

Middle America, on the contrary, has had an essential and striking role in the development of the faunas of all the Americas. A few admirable studies of the static, modern zoogeography of parts of the region have been made, and some attention has been given to historical aspects, but full evaluation is lacking and too little thought has been given to this subject. A cause for relative neglect has been the extreme paucity of primary historical documents. Pre-Pleistocene nonaquatic fossils are rare in tropical Middle America. There is a rather small but extremely important early Pliocene mammalian local fauna from Honduras (found and described by P. O. McGrew and associates), and there are several scattered Pleistocene faunules of considerable interest but still lacking forms (especially the smaller mammals) that would be more fully enlightening. Recently, several Miocene mammals, not yet fully published, have been found in Panama.

Direct and conclusive study will require a good sequence of Central American land faunas, including vertebrate microfaunas, from Miocene, at latest, to recent. There is no assurance, nor even any considerable probability, that such a sequence remains to be discovered. It is nevertheless possible to evaluate the role of this region with some assurance, even if without adequate detail, on the basis of the scraps of local, direct evidence and the increasingly imposing array of indirect evidence.

The recent fauna of Central America is essentially like that of South America. The same faunal strata occur there, although, as already noted, their ages and relationshsips with respect to the area occupied are different here. Environmental conditions in Central America are similar to those of adjacent tropical South

America. With union of these two areas, the resulting neotropical fauna has occupied territory as far as the environmental similarity extends. This is roughly as far as the climate can be called "tropical" in broad terms, and the line conventionally bounding the Neotropical Region to the north has been drawn at the equally conventional boundary of tropical climates, delimiting an area extending to and stopping with the hot Mexican lowlands. This is, indeed, merely a critical line within a broad transitional zone and not a localized barrier. Few distributions stop precisely at the line. Starting far north of it, say in Colorado or New Mexico, and progressing to regions far south of it, say to Ecuador or the Guianas, animals mainly neotropical in distribution rather steadily become more frequent, and those mainly nearctic less frequent. In detail, Central America also has local differentiation, with numerous species and some genera (but no higher categories among mammals and few among other animals) confined to that area.

The place of Central America within the broad outlines of static recent zoogeography is well displayed by comparison of the mammalian families of New Mexico, Costa Rica, and the Guianas, each area with the same number of families (21). About half the families (10 fully and 2 more marginally) are common to all three areas but generally with different species and sometimes with different genera in each. Six families occur in New Mexico only, as among these three areas, and 3 in the Guianas only. These are the most definitely nearctic and neotropical groups, respectively. Costa Rica has no families that do not occur either in New Mexico or in the Guianas. It has 3 families in common with New Mexico but not the Guianas and 6 with the Guianas but not New Mexico, and is thus intermediate in this respect but somewhat more like the Guianas, justifiying inclusion in the Neotropical Region.

Middle America may be considered statically as a transition zone and historically as, successively or intermittently, a barrier and a migration route, but these simple and usual characterizations hardly begin to express its true role and importance.

As a transition zone and migration route, the role is not merely that of a habitat and a pathway. Middle America is a faunal filter. (See Fig. 45.) Its ecological characteristics, in the broadest sense, determined which stocks were involved in faunal interchanges between North and South America and which are now immobilized

FAMILIES OF RECENT LAND MAMMALS IN SELECTED PARTS OF NORTH, CENTRAL, AND SOUTH AMERICA

| | *New Mexico* | *Costa Rica* | *Guianas* |
|---|---|---|---|
| Didelphidae | X | X | X |
| Soricidae | X | X | O |
| Cebidae | O | X | X |
| Callithricidae | O | O | X |
| Myrmecophagidae | O | X | X |
| Bradypodidae | O | X | X |
| Dasypodidae | X * | X | X |
| Ochotonidae | X | O | O |
| Leporidae | X | X | X |
| Sciuridae | X | X | X |
| Geomyidae | X | X | O |
| Heteromyidae | X | X | O |
| Castoridae | X | O | O |
| Cricetidae | X | X | X |
| Zapodidae | X | O | O |
| Erethizontidae | X | X | X |
| Caviidae | O | O | X |
| Hydrochoeridae | O | O | X |
| Dasyproctidae | O | X | X |
| Echimyidae | O | X | X |
| Canidae | X | X | X |
| Ursidae | X | O | O † |
| Procyonidae | X | X | X |
| Mustelidae | X | X | X |
| Felidae | X | X | X |
| Tapiridae | O | X | X |
| Tayassuidae | X * | X | X |
| Cervidae | X | X | X |
| Antilocapridae | X | O | O |
| Bovidae | X | O | O |

X Present. O Absent. * Present but marginal. † Absent here, but present elsewhere equally deep in South America.

to north and to south. The filtering action is not sharply localized. It begins well to the north (and west), roughly at the edge of the lower Sonoran life zone in southwest United States, and also reaches far to the south and east, more or less to the edge of the Guiana highlands and thence southward and westward. From these quite indefinite outer edges, the filtering action becomes denser toward the central critical line, which now approximates the border of the central Mexican plateau. It probably had about the same or at times a more southerly position in the Pleistocene, but in parts of the Tertiary it may have been considerably farther north.

At present some northern groups, such as the shrews, pocket mice, and pocket gophers, penetrate well into the filter zone, but not beyond its vague southeastern edge. Others, such as the bob-cats, bison, and sheep, have stopped near its attenuated northern border. For other northern forms the filter zone has been essentially an open passage: rabbits, squirrels, dogs, otters, pumas, and many others among recent animals, and also horses, mastodons, and some other fairly recently extinct groups. Most of the old south-erners, South American mammals of the first and second faunal strata, are now stopped somewhere within the zone: most armadil-los, all anteaters and tree sloths, all the old native South American rodents except the porcupines. One armadillo (*Dasypus novem-cinctus*) is peculiar in that a generation or so ago it stopped at about the northern edge of the filter zone but in the last few years has spread well beyond this. A related form (*Dasypus bellus*, now extinct) was even more widespread in North America in the Pleistocene, when there were also a few other old southerners (glyptodonts, ground sloths, capybaras) unaffected by the filter. It is also interesting that the filter was in some cases permeable for ancestral forms but now completely separates their differentiated northern and southern descendants; for instance, in the cases of the porcupines and the bears.

Most peculiar in this respect are the rather numerous animals clearly of ultimate northern origin and yet now stopped in or *south* of the filter zone: coatis, kinkajous, the numerous kinds of South American cats other than the puma, short-faced bears, tapirs,

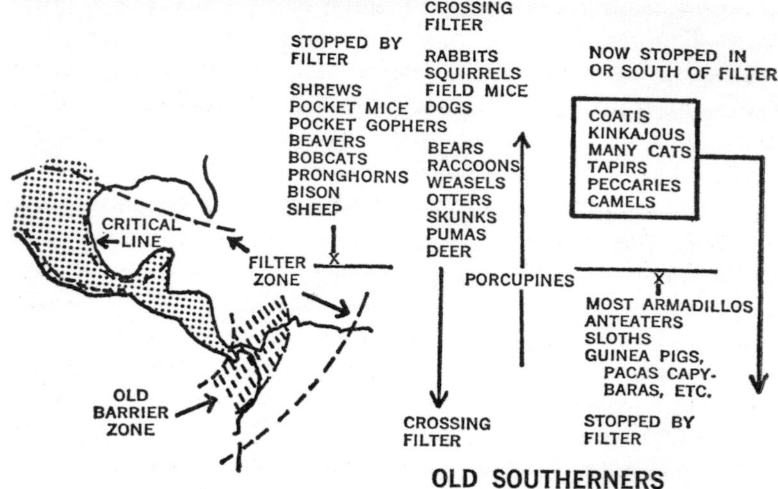


Fig. 45. Diagram of Middle America as a faunal filter. The examples given are from the recent fauna of land mammals. For some groups the action of the filter was different in the Pleistocene.

peccaries (reaching the extreme northern edge of the filter, but hardly beyond), camels, and other lesser differentiates. Superficially one can say simply that such groups happened to become extinct in North but not in South America, a statement but not an explanation. For most of them, at least, there is a more explanatory probability: the particular populations and lines involved were native to Middle America, adapted to environmental conditions prevailing there and over much of South America and not adapted to or *immediately* derived from North America above the present filter zone. In some cases there are complications requiring modification of or additions to this general theory (for instance, for the bears, páramo tapirs, and camels), but even these need not be flatly exceptional or contradictory, and for most groups involved the theory is a simple, elegant, and sufficient explanation of their peculiar distributional history.

It is an obvious but nevertheless frequently unappreciated fact that immigrants from North to South America did not come from the continent as a whole or from its broad, now temperate zone, best known to us both paleontologically and neontologically, but only from Central America. With local and geologically brief interruptions for part of it, Central America has been continuous with the North American land mass throughout the Cenozoic. Marine barriers were mostly in the extreme southeastern part of Central America, and the major barrier, especially toward the end of the Cenozoic, was in what is now part of South, not Central, America (in western Colombia). Thus Central or broadly Middle America must have had a fauna mainly or purely North American in origin and in broad faunal type until toward the end of the Pliocene, a conclusion attested by the Pliocene fauna from Honduras and Miocene finds from Panama, all entirely North American in affinities. Nevertheless, Middle America must have been an important center of regional faunal differentiation within the North American general fauna.

Even in the early Cenozoic, when climatic zoning was less sharp than now, such zoning did exist, and Middle America has by astronomical and meteorological necessity always been the warmest (or most evenly warm) and tropical part of North America. It must long have been a center of adaptation and local radiation of faunal elements specifically adapted to its special conditions, not only climatic but also edaphic, floral, etc. This special local fauna was the one, and the only one, available for spread to South America in all of the faunal strata of the latter region. Some Central American differentiates have succeeded in spreading northward (jaguars in the Pleistocene, for instance, and probably a number of otherwise mysterious newcomers in more northern fossil fields throughout the Cenozoic). Spread southward, when geographically possible, was more general and rapid because northern South America is more like Middle America in climate and associated factors. The Tertiary sea barrier did not follow a climatic zonal boundary, and when connection was established the incorporation of Central America into the South American and of South America into the Central American faunal zone was rapid and reciprocal.

It thus becomes explicable that within many groups of old northern origin there are differentiated neotropical lines, the roots of which have not been found among the fossils from higher latitudes in North America. The more distinctively neotropical forms (at levels mainly of specific to generic differentiation) in many families may be inferred to have been Middle American differentiates: numerous noncaviomorph rodents, some dogs, the southern procyonids (*sensu lato*), most of the southern cats and most of the deer, among others. There is also discernible, on these grounds, a minor stratification *within* the broad late stratum of the South American fauna, between forms which had been longer in Middle America and more differentiated there, and those newer or less isolated in that region. Thus the coatis (*Nasua*) are inferred to be older and their allies the true raccoons (*Procyon*) younger Middle American forms, or among the deer the brockets (*Mazama*) may be older and the closer allies of our white-tails (*Odocoileus*) younger there. In some such cases there are other factors to consider, especially the possibility and timing of spread northward from Middle America. Here emphasis can only be placed on broader aspects of the historical role of Middle America and details cannot further be discussed. In fact, these details have not yet been adequately studied, if at all, from this point of view.

• • •

# PART 7

*In the concluding section, all the southern continents—Australia, Africa, and South America—are examined on a comparative basis, from the standpoints of climate, geology, and faunal (mammalian) background.*

*The origins, developmental stages, migrations, and extinctions of various orders, families, and species are discussed, including the troublesome question of gigantism, in its applicability to the problem of survival.*

*Land and water barriers to faunal interchange are resurveyed and, finally, the basic importance to science as a whole of studying the great land masses of the south is emphasized by example.*

• • •

# Mammalian Evolution on the Southern Continents

The three most distinctive mammalian faunal regions, Ethiopian, Australian, and Neotropical, approximately correspond with the three southern geographic continents. They include most of the tropical land area of the world, but each also lies partly in the south temperate zone. They have other features in common, and yet each is unique in many respects. Those resemblances and differences make their consideration together particularly interesting and instructive. Data on the mammals of each continent separately were provided by a recent symposium.* The present essay brings that information into a common framework, supplies some other materials, and also discusses some moot points.

## CENOZOIC GEOGRAPHIC HISTORY OF THE SOUTHERN CONTINENTS

Mammalian evolution was largely Mesozoic in terms of elapsed time. However, we know almost nothing of unquestionable

* Papers delivered at this symposium have not been published in full; extended abstracts are cited at the end of this section.

Mesozoic mammals on the southern continents (a single late Jurassic specimen from Africa), and not enough anywhere to give a connected account in zoogeographic terms. Moreover, the differentiation of continental faunas and origin of recent faunas are Cenozoic events and can be considered without worrying too much about Mesozoic antecedents, much as we would like to know the latter. Most of this discussion is therefore limited to the Cenozoic.

Throughout much of their history, the southern continents seem to have been more stable than the northern, and this is particularly true in the Cenozoic. All are built around large Pre-Cambrian shields. Areas of marked tectonic instability have been marginal in all: eastern Australia in the Paleozoic; northern Africa in Mesozoic and Cenozoic (plus Cenozoic rifting in east Africa); western South America in the Cenozoic. All had extensive epicontinental seas in the Cretaceous, but these had withdrawn by the end of that period. Cenozoic seas on all three were small and strictly marginal and made no really important differences in either the areas or the outlines of the continents. We may thus consider all three as units not essentially different from the present in those particular respects throughout our story. (Summary in Kummel, 1961.)

It may now also be taken without serious doubt that the three southern continents had approximately the same geographic relationships to each other, to the northern continents, and to the poles and equator throughout the Cenozoic. That statement was often disputed in the past, and there is a large literature both geological and biogeographical claiming the contrary. Specifically, various conflicting theories of continental drift, land bridges, and transoceanic continents have involved intercontinental land connections in the Southern Hemisphere during the Cenozoic. If so, the mammals themselves peculiarly took no advantage of them, and indeed the land mammals provide conclusive evidence against any such connections (e.g., Simpson, 1943, 1953). Even the new paleomagnetic data, which raise such serious doubts as regards earlier times, confirm that the southern continents have been at least near their present positions throughout the Cenozoic (e.g., Cox and

Doell, 1960). Whatever may prove to be true for other organisms or earlier times, it should really now be taken without argument that there has been no direct connection of terrestrial mammalian faunas between any two southern continents during the Cenozoic.

The faunal connections that are real and pertinent are between southern continents and the northern lands still now geographically closest to them: Australia with southeastern Asia; Africa with Europe and southwestern Asia; South America with North America. In all three cases, those connections have been both incomplete and intermittent. They have never permitted full intermingling of faunas, and each continent was wholly isolated for long periods of time. In other respects, the pertinent relationships have differed markedly for the three southern continents. It is highly improbable that Australia has had a continuous land connection with Asia since some time well back in the Mesozoic. Throughout that time, however, there has been a series of island steppingstones, highly changeable but continuously present in one form or another. Sometime in the late Mesozoic or earliest Cenozoic, South America had either a land bridge or fairly traversable steppingstones to North America. Thereafter it was isolated by a significant sea barrier until latest Pliocene or earliest Pleistocene, when continuous land connection with North America was established (or re-established). Africa has been the least isolated southern continent. During much of the Cenozoic it was indeed cut off from Eurasia, except Arabia, which is geologically part of Africa. There were, however, intermittent connections, and faunal interchange has been extensive at various times even though not continuous or complete. The Tethyan barrier furthermore seems to have been narrow in some places, at least, and it was probably not an absolute obstacle.

Those Cenozoic geographic relationships have produced some of the important features shared by the southern continents as regards mammalian evolution. For land mammals the continents have all been zoogeographic dead ends—that is, each has had only one way in or out. Each has also been a separate center of mammalian evolution where isolation has generated autochthons to high taxonomic levels and endemicity has been constantly great.

Although this is an evolutionary factor that they share, its result has been that they share extremely little in terms of actual taxa (genera, species, etc.).

## ECOLOGICAL CHANGES

Although the southern continents have been so stable geographically, they have undergone some great changes in topography, climate, vegetation, and other features that may be subsumed as ecological. Such changes were to some extent parallel on the three, but some were peculiar to each.

On all three there is sufficient evidence that climatic zoning became more pronounced from early to late Cenozoic and that warm temperate to cool climates have moved nearer to the equator (e.g., Gill, 1961). It is less clear but probable that there was some rise of average temperature, or some poleward extension of tropical and subtropical climates, from early to middle Tertiary and thereafter a more pronounced reversed movement. All three continents underwent extreme fluctuations of temperature and precipitation in the Pleistocene. During glacial episodes, all developed local mountain glaciers, but none had continental icecaps, and glaciation *per se* had little effect on their faunas.

On all three continents rainfall was formerly, if not greater, at least more evenly distributed than it is at present. All now have extensive deserts and semideserts, but these developed late in the Cenozoic and are comparatively recent habitats. It is therefore probable that the animals now occurring in them were derived from those of other ecological zones and represent relatively late adaptations to arid environments. In other respects the arid regions of the three continents have quite different roles. The greater part of Australia is now occupied by the central deserts and semideserts; other ecological zones form mere (but broad) margins to north, east, and south. Older kinds of habitats have therefore become restricted to those marginal areas, and even there they have undergone marked ecological change. The *Eucalyptus-Acacia* associations of the present wooded margins of Australia apparently became dominant there only in the Pleistocene and are not old (Gill, 1961, and personal communications).

In South America the most arid regions (central Pacific coast; northwestern Argentina; Patagonian *mesetas*) are marginal. Their faunas are an attenuated sampling of the general continental fauna, derived in the late Cenozoic from those of adjacent savannahs and, in part, woodlands. It is, I think, a mistake to regard the Patagonian *mesetas* as a plateau or highland or to consider them a source area for mammals of other habitats. They are not significantly higher than adjacent plains, savannahs and grasslands, and differ from them only in being more arid and windswept. It also seems clear that adaptive evolutionary movement has been into them and not in the reverse direction as these conditions arose in and since the late Tertiary. Earlier in the Tertiary Patagonia was woodland and savannah, and it then shared, but probably did not originate, faunas of ecological types now restricted to less rigorous regions.

The deserts of southern and southwestern Africa and of Somaliland are also marginal and are analogous to those of South America in their ecological relationships and faunal histories. The vast northern desert zone of Africa, on the other hand, has become a major barrier or strong filter between two rich and very different faunas, each of which penetrates it to a strictly limited extent. Its effectiveness as a barrier is increased by the fact that it runs east and west from ocean to ocean with temperate climates to the north and tropical to the south. It is now the boundary between two main zoogeographic regions, with the truly African or Ethiopian fauna strongly confined to the south of it. That was not true in the early and middle Cenozoic, when conditions and faunas over the whole geographic continent (then including Arabia) were more uniform.

As regards mountains and their effects on faunas, the three continents offer more contrasts than resemblances. Australia has had no high mountains during the Cenozoic but only marginal wooded uplands of moderate elevation. Until the late Cenozoic desiccation of the interior, the uplands cannot have been so different ecologically from the rest of the continent, and their present fauna probably represents in considerable part a survival of what was formerly a more general kind of assemblage. The northern coastal mountains of Africa have a rather similar relationship to older north African habitats and to the adjacent now arid zone. The volcanic peaks of central and eastern Africa reach great heights, but they are both too recent and too scattered to have served as centers of evolution for a distinctive faunal facies. East African highlands do to some extent have relicts or outliers of faunal elements not adapted to the surrounding, now more arid, habitats.

South America, alone among the southern continents, has a high, long, continuous *cordillera* (chain of mountains). The ecological effects of the Andes began in the Miocene and have increased sporadically ever since, reaching the present maximum only in the Quaternary. The high *páramo* or *altiplano* regions, with cold temperate to almost polar climates, represent one of the most recent habitats in South America and can only have been populated by mammals whose ancestors lived at lower elevations and in quite different habitats. The lower warm temperate and tropical flanks of the Andes are similar and adjacent to non-Andine uplands and tropical lowlands and have simply retained or received from the latter ecologically equivalent faunas. It is hardly possible that the older mammals of the Brazilian uplands were derived from the Andes, as has been suggested, because those uplands were there and surely occupied by mammals of the older faunal stocks before the Andes existed. The more distinctive cold temperate parts of the Andes have faunas now continuous with and similar to those of southern cold temperate uplands, through Patagonia to Tierra del Fuego.

In both sub-Saharan Africa and South America the most widespread Recent habitats are those of lowland rain forests and moderately elevated woodlands with lateral and interior patches of savannah. Such habitats also cover most of New Guinea but occur only in a marginal and relictual way in Australia proper. In all three regions there is strong evidence that these habitats represent an ecological complex that has existed throughout the Cenozoic and was formerly even more widespread than now. They are in fact the oldest and most continuously present of all habitats on these continents. It therefore seems to me reasonably certain that they have been the principal centers of evolution and that adaptive spread of mammals has predominantly, although not exclusively, been out from and not in to them. It has been suggested that the major tropical lowland of South America, the Orinoco-Amazon-Paraná system of basins, was occupied by a mediterranean sea during much of the Cenozoic and that its present terrestrial fauna moved in relatively recently from surrounding highlands. Geological evidence conclusively disproves this and shows that apart from minor estuarine incursions these basins have been freshwater and more or less as at present throughout the Cenozoic. (See, e.g., Jenks, 1956; supposed evidence of marine Pliocene in the upper Amazon basin has since been found to be incorrect, Simpson, 1961 a.)

## FAUNAL ORIGINS

The ecological conditions on the various continents have obviously affected the evolution of mammals within each. Ecological similarities among the continents have also been a factor in convergent evolution. Ecology has, however, little to do with the fact that the faunas of the three continents are extremely different taxonomically, and have been so, at times to even greater degree, throughout the Cenozoic. These differences are caused by two other factors: (1) the three southern continents had quite different basic stocks of mammals around the beginning of the Cenozoic, and (2) there has been no direct interchange of land mammals between any two of them and all the possible indirect routes have had multiple, strong barriers.

Although the evidence is quite incomplete, it is probable that the earliest Cenozoic mammalian faunas were basically similar in Eurasia and North America. They included: primitive marsupials (didelphoids); a variety of quite generalized insectivorelike placentals, some of which were evolving toward more specialized Insectivora, strictly speaking, and some toward primates; other primitive animals whose descendants were to specialize as carnivores; a variety of ancestral ungulate herbivores, some primitive and some prematurely specializing in various details; and several other placental offshoots mostly destined to rather early extinction. Approximately the whole earliest third of the Cenozoic mammalian record is unknown in Africa, but by projection backward from later faunas and by other indirect evidence, it is highly probable that Africa also early acquired a fauna of that same general type. The actual places of origin or directions of first movement of the elements of those faunas are entirely unknown, but it is fairly certain that relatively unselective early faunal spread occurred in one direction or the other, or both, between Eurasia (most likely Europe) and Africa.

South America and especially Australia, unlike Africa, shared only limited elements of what may be called the World Continent fauna of the early Cenozoic. South America had only three basic stocks: marsupials, edentates, and ungulates. Primitive members of all three groups were also present in the Paleocene of North America, although edentates are not yet known there in the very earliest Paleocene faunas. In the North American Paleocene there are also numerous other groups entirely unknown in early South American faunas. There was clearly some selective faunal connection between the two continents in the latest Cretaceous or earliest Paleocene. It is possible that one or more of its three basic stocks originated in South America and thence spread northward, but the present consensus is that they probably originated somewhere on the World Continent and moved from North to South America. The much less diverse nature of the basic South American fauna indicates that spread was through a strong semi-barrier, but whether this involved a filter bridge or one or more overwater hops is uncertain.

The whole Australian Tertiary mammal record is extremely poor and that of the early Tertiary is virtually nil. It is, however, likely that only primitive marsupials were shared with the World Continent around the beginning of the Cenozoic. Again the direction of spread is not really known, but the strong probability is that it was from Asia to Australia. *Only* primitive marsupials (perhaps only a single species) then followed that route, even though other mammals were already rather abundant and varied on the World Continent. That must indicate waif dispersal over a very strong barrier, and the most likely way is by island-hopping along the Indonesian arc. The fact that both Australia and South America, and they alone, became major centers of marsupial evolution was long cited as evidence of direct faunal connection. It is, however, now clear that the two marsupial radiations were completely independent and that all they share is their roots in the most primitive didelphoid stock. Primitive didelphoids are known to have been rather abundant in the Cretaceous of North America, at least, and in the early Tertiary of North America and Europe, at least. It is highly probable that they spread separately from the north to Australia and to South America.

## CENOZOIC EVOLUTION

After the original stocking, faunal changes on all three continents involved two major processes: the radiation and further evolution *in situ* of the original stocks, and the spread into the continents of other stocks from the north. In each case the original stocks occupied large, varied, and isolated continents, and in each they underwent rather rapid basic adaptive divergence. In Africa that was most striking among the ungulates, several groups of which became so distinct as to be classified as autochthonous orders: Proboscidea, Embrithopoda, Hyracoidea, Tubulidentata. In South America a similar and in some respects remarkably parallel but entirely separate ungulate radiation gave rise to the Litopterna, Xenungulata, Pyrotheria, Astrapotheria, and Notoungulata. In South America the marsupials and edentates also underwent basic radiations, giving rise to several superfamilies and more families in each, into ecological zones and niches occupied by insectivores, rodents, carnivores, and some other early placental orders in Africa and the northern continents. In Australia the marsupials, alone, radiated to occupy much but not all of the ecological gamut covered by marsupials, edentates, and ungulates in South America and by the numerous placental orders in Africa and the northern world. Although the pertinent fossil record is lacking, that basic radiation in Australia undoubtedly gave rise to all three Quaternary superfamilies and probably to most or all of the families. (The few Tertiary mammals so far described from Australia all belong to Quaternary families and even subfamilies.) Monotremes were probably present in Australia before marsupials appeared there and they may well also have had an early radiation later largely overlaid by that of the marsupials, but at present there is no known evidence of this one way or the other.

In South America clearly and in Africa probably an exuberant basal radiation was followed by a thinning out of many of the early divergent lines as others established themselves efficiently in the main ecological zones. There is no evidence from Australia in this respect. In all three continents, but at different times and to different degrees, faunal evolution was eventually profoundly modified by incursion of new groups from the north. As already noted, this was most extensive and frequent in Africa. There were extensive interchanges with, and not only immigrations from, Eurasia at all taxonomic levels. Those episodes are most clearly indicated in the late Oligocene to early Miocene, earliest Pliocene (or late Miocene as some geologists divide the epochs), and early Pleistocene. It is, however, probable that there was frequent sporadic or continual interchange of single groups in addition to those more extensive faunal movements. The result was that although Africa was sufficiently isolated to have its own distinct faunal complexion, mostly below the family level, faunal evolution there was not independent from that in southern Europe and Asia. In broader view, the changes were similar to those on the northern continents. Among those changes were the early appearance and subsequent great expansion of primates and rodents, replacement of creodonts by more modernized carnivores, and partial replacement of older ungulates by perissodactyls and, especially, artiodactyls.

South America remained isolated almost or quite until the end of the Tertiary, but during that interval two new groups appeared there: rodents, known from the early Oligocene, and primates, from the latest Oligocene. This is a minor point, but I think it unlikely that these two reached South America at the same time. Both groups radiated greatly, the rodents much more than the primates, to some extent replacing ecologically similar members of the more ancient stocks but apparently also occupying many niches to which the latter had not become adapted. When they appear in the record both give evidence of prior, but not long prior, unified ancestry and both are monophyletic taxa, the rodent suborder Caviomorpha and the monkey superfamily Ceboidea. Because these rodents resemble some Old World, especially African, forms and the monkeys also resemble those of Africa and Asia, it was formerly widely believed that one or both of these groups was in fact derived from Africa. It is, however, now generally accepted that this is an example of parallelism, the similar South American and African forms having originated separately but from related ancestors present in the Eocene in North America and Eurasia, respectively.

The isolation of South America was so nearly complete and so long-continued that toward the end of the Tertiary most of the orders and all of the families of nonvolant (non-flying) land mammals were endemic. Fossil bats are almost unknown from South America, and some of their families may not then have been endemic, but 56% of the Recent families and 87% of the Recent genera are Neotropical endemics, so that South American endemicity in the Miocene was probably also high. When the land connection with North America was established, or re-established, around the end of the Pliocene, there was a great interchange of faunas. Deer, camels, peccaries, horses, tapirs, mastodonts, cats, dogs, raccoons (and other procyonids), weasels (and allies), cricetid rodents, squirrels, and rabbits spread widely from North to

South America. The number of taxa at all levels was greatly increased by this influx and the fauna became oversaturated, with numerous ecological duplicates or competitors. Wholesale extinction ensued, affecting mostly the older southern groups. The number of Recent taxa may still be somewhat greater than the Pliocene, but it has decreased from the Pleistocene high to about the Pliocene order of magnitude. In terms of numbers of taxa and their ecological variety, the fauna seems now again to be in balance within itself and with its environments. The cricetid rodents in particular diversified greatly and rapidly on reaching South America. In part they replaced competing caviomorphs, but they were also involved in a different and more detailed parceling out of niches. As a result of this faunal incursion, the most dramatic that the world has ever seen, about half of the present South American mammalian fauna (in terms of genera) has developed from late Pliocene or Quaternary North American invaders, about 35% is of mid-Tertiary North American ancestry, and only about 15% is derived from the early Tertiary South American stocks. (Simpson, 1950; Part 6 of this book.)

No fossil bats have been described from Australia, but analysis of the Recent fauna and indirect evidence strongly suggest that bats did reach Australia early in the Cenozoic, perhaps in the Eocene, and that they have been drifting down the island steppingstones intermittently ever since. There may have been 20 or 30 successive immigrations into the Australian Region, all clearly derived from Asia via Indonesia. They have undergone little further evolution or radiation, and what has occurred at specific or rarely generic levels has been centered on New Guinea rather than Australia itself. None of the Australian families and only 29% of the genera are endemic. This low endemicity can be imputed in part to the mobility of these flying animals, but in greater part to the fact that the west-east migration route from southeast Asia (earlier including Sumatra, Java, and Borneo as parts of the continent) to New Guinea lies in the same climatic zone and has had only minor ecological barriers throughout, despite the continuous presence of sea barriers. In contrast with Australia the Neotropical bats have become and remained highly endemic because the north-south route there crosses decidedly different climatic and ecological zones.

Murid rodents have reached the Australian Region from Asia by island-hopping in several different waves, probably starting in the Miocene. Like the bats, all reached Australia via New Guinea. Unlike the bats, descendants of some of the earlier immigrants have radiated markedly both in New Guinea and in Australia, to generic and even subfamily levels. Seventy-seven per cent of the 13 continental Australian genera are endemic. Apart from the monotremes, marsupials, bats, and most murids, all the other Australian mammals have been introduced by man. (On Australian mammals in general, see Simpson, 1961 b; Part 5 of this book.)

## INFLUENCE OF SOUTHERN ON NORTHERN FAUNAS

Australia has been in the fullest sense a dead end. It is conceivable that some of its marsupials have reached Asia (Mc Kenna, personal communication), but there is no published evidence to that effect, and in any event they had no important or lasting effect on the Asiatic fauna. As noted above, in contrast to Australia there has been a great deal of intermittent spread of mammals from Africa to Eurasia. By the later Tertiary numerous groups of probable African origin, such as the aardvarks, mastodonts, hyracoids, giraffes, hippopotami, and some bovids, were also widespread in southern Europe and Asia. Most of these have since become extinct in Eurasia, giving the impression that a more or less Pliocene fauna survives in Africa although in fact the fauna there has also changed greatly since the Pliocene. There is still considerable resemblance between Africa and southern Asia, involving such groups as primates, certain rodents, hyaenas, cats, civets, elephants, rhinoceroses, and again some bovids. However, some at least of the shared taxa moved from Eurasia to Africa rather than the reverse, and all of them may have. The influence of the African fauna on the present Oriental fauna is therefore uncertain and may be slight.

North Africa, until relatively recently including what is now the

Arabian peninsula, was faunally Ethiopian during most of the Cenozoic. It was, however, also a transition zone, being the source area for all African mammals that spread to Eurasia and the area first occupied by Eurasian immigrants. Climatically and in some other ecological respects it has long resembled southern Europe and southwestern Asia more than Central Africa. With the late Cenozoic development of the desert barrier, the African fauna, strictly speaking, has been confined to the mainly tropical sub-Sahara. Temperate North Africa, although still with a strong Ethiopian faunal element, has more in common with temperate Eurasia and is almost always included in the Palearctic Region.

Between North and South America something like the inverse has occurred, and this has been subject to some confusion in faunal studies. Tropical North America, formerly Nearctic, has come to be conventionally part of the Neotropical Region, just as temperate North Africa, formerly Ethiopian, has conventionally become part of the Palearctic Region. Throughout the Tertiary, Central America was geographically part of North America and separated by sea from South America. (The major and most enduring sea barrier was not in Central America but in what is now Colombia.) Moreover, during that period the ecological contrast between what is now tropical Central America and what is now temperate North America was far less than it is now. Although the direct fossil evidence is still exiguous, it confirms the strong indirect evidence that Central America had a strictly Nearctic fauna until about the end of the Pliocene. Southern North America was a region of some local differentiation of Nearctic stocks where species, genera, and even some higher taxa arose in adaptation to tropical and subtropical conditions. With the fluctuating late Tertiary-Quaternary movement southward of the tropical-temperate boundary zone, some of those groups became more nearly confined to the south and eventually to Central America and now tropical Mexico. It was obviously the fauna of this area, and not that of present temperate North America, that came into contact with the South American fauna when the continents were united. Environmentally there was then more in common between tropical South America and tropical

North America than between the latter and temperate North America. There was, therefore, rather thorough admixture of the two previously entirely different tropical faunas. The effects of this admixture became rapidly attenuated northward and tended to ebb and flow with Quaternary climatic fluctuations.

Neomammalogists customarily speak of faunal "affinities" in terms of where the most closely related and abundant relatives of faunal elements live today. In those terms, which are of course valid and useful as descriptions of a present, static situation, it is perfectly true that the predominant affinities of the tropical North American fauna are with South America. That is, of course, the basis on which the present Neotropical Region is delimited. However, much the greater part of the tropical North American (Central American and tropical Mexican) fauna is autochthonous there (or elsewhere in North America) and not in South America. In dynamic, historical terms, this is in fact predominantly a tropical Nearctic fauna. It would be more indicative of the true situation, both static and dynamic, to say that the South American fauna has largely Central American affinities rather than the reverse. The contrasts in point of view are well illustrated by summary analysis of Burt's (1949) listing of the 55 genera (his count) of tropical Mexican mammals. From the static point of view, 49% of the genera have southern affinities, 29% have northern affinities, and 22% are endemic. From the dynamic point of view, 78% are (largely tropical) Nearctic autochthons and only 22% are South American autochthons. Southern affinities, both static and dynamic, of course increase southward, but even in Colombia and Venezuela the affinities of the recent fauna are largely tropical North American.

The effect of the autochthonous South American fauna on that of temperate North America has been and remains slight. During the warmer parts of the Pleistocene the only South American autochthons known to have spread into what is now the United States are as follows: one marsupial; several ground sloths (probably four valid genera); two glyptodonts (probably); two genera of armadillos; and two genera of caviomorph rodents. Only three mammals of stocks immigrant from South America still occur north of Mexico (an opossum, an armadillo, and a porcupine), and two of those, although spreading at present, are mostly confined to warm climates. It has been said that numerous other "Neotropical" genera are now advancing into the Nearctic Region, but that is a somewhat misleading statement. The genera in question (e.g. *Nasua, Tayassu*) are in fact Nearctic autochthons only recently incorporated into the Neotropical fauna, and they are simply spreading back within their native fauna in consequence of ecological reversions. This discussion excludes bats because of uncertainty as to which are in fact of South American and which of southern North American origin, but there is no evident reason why they would be exceptions to the generalization clearly true of other mammals.

## PLEISTOCENE-RECENT TRANSITIONS AND EXTINCTIONS

All the continents, both northern and southern, had more diverse faunas in the Pleistocene than at present. Obviously this involves Pleistocene-Recent extinctions, local and general. As regards the smaller Recent faunas, they may imply either negative faunal imbalance, with some niches becoming empty, or ecological impoverishment, with some niches disappearing. As regards the larger Pleistocene faunas, it may imply either positive faunal imbalance, with overlapping within niches, or ecological enrichment, with more niches than at present. It is also pertinent to consider whether the Pleistocene faunas were abnormally large, or whether they represented only a continuation of, or even a decline from, earlier levels. The Pleistocene high may to some extent be illusory, because heightened faunal turnover and frequent changes of range under the greatly fluctuating conditions of that epoch, along with imprecision of dating and association records, can give the effect of larger faunas than actually occurred at any one time in any one area. Nevertheless it seems practically certain that during the latter part, at least, of the Pleistocene and the Recent extinction of taxa at all levels has exceeded their origination and that there has everywhere been a real decline in diversity.

Although all three southern continents exhibit this (indeed, worldwide) phenomenon, its intensity and circumstances seem to have been markedly different on the three. Africa seems definitely to have undergone the least decrease. The Pleistocene data for Africa are fairly good, but they are markedly deficient for small mammals, which have been less liable to extinction on the average. They are also hard to evaluate because some species in the published lists may be based on merely individual variants and some genera listed as extinct are nevertheless extant in different form or are based on extinct species that some students would not consider generically distinct. It appears that comparatively few middle Pleistocene genera, not over a third among the larger mammals and considerably less among the small ones, are without modern descendants. The late Pleistocene fauna is quite like the Recent, and mass late Pleistocene-Recent extinction did not occur. The African fauna does merit its reputation as a survival from the prehistoric, but from the Pleistocene, not the Tertiary. Nevertheless the early and early-middle Pleistocene did have a number of mammals, mostly large and bizarre, that are extinct without issue. The Pliocene fauna is too poorly known to warrant any firm conclusion, but I have the impression that there was a continuing buildup of fauna culminating in the early Pleistocene. This seems to have been due both to evolution within Africa and to incursions from Eurasia. For example, the equids are not known in Africa until the early Pleistocene and were clearly more diverse in early to middle Pleistocene (probably at least eight species) than they are now (one species of ass and three of zebras).

The present African fauna seems to be approximately in balance. It has about the number and diversity of species to be expected if faunal size is near equilibrium. It is, indeed, the richest of all continental faunas, and that might suggest a positive imbalance, but the continent is large, ecologically varied, and mostly tropical. It is well known that almost all groups of organisms are most diversified in the tropics, although this has not been fully explained, to my satisfaction at least. More studies are needed on possible competitive interference of the many species of bovids, especially, but it is unlikely that many of these would be doomed to early extinction by competition under natural conditions. (That human activities are decimating the fauna, directly and especially indirectly, is a different matter.) On the other side of the picture, few, if any, available niches seem now to be unoccupied.

In South America the available data give the impression that diversity of the two earlier faunal strata, descendants of the basic Cenozoic fauna and of the mid-Tertiary island-hoppers, reached a maximum sometime in the Miocene and was declining somewhat in the Pliocene. That may be an artifact of classification and discovery, but there is no doubt that the Pleistocene faunas were much richer than those either of the Pliocene or of the Recent. That was caused almost entirely by the incursion of so many North American groups and by the fact that some of them, notably the cricetids, then diversified rapidly and extensively within South America. Although this is not so well documented, diversification at low taxonomic levels was doubtless also stimulated by the opening up and spread of comparatively new Andine, desert, and cool temperate environments.

In South America there has been mass extinction through the late Pleistocene and early Recent. This has affected both Pleistocene immigrants and older South American groups, but especially the latter. The Recent fauna, although nominally impoverished in comparison with the positively imbalanced Pleistocene fauna, seems simply to have returned to at least an approximate balance. Available tabulations for the two continents are not reliably comparable, but they suggest that South America now has about three-fifths as many mammalian species as Africa, and that is the same ratio as their areas. The majority of niches, at least, are well occupied in South America, even though some minor niche differentiation may still be in progress.

The Australian Tertiary fauna is much too scantily known for meaningful comparison with that of the Pleistocene. It may be significant that no striking pre-Pleistocene novelties have turned up, for that is consistent, as far as it goes, with the hypothesis that there was no decline of diversity before the Pleistocene. There has been a marked decline and mass extinction from Pleistocene, probably late Pleistocene, to now. There is suggestive evidence that some negative imbalance has resulted, that although all the available broad ecological categories are represented, some are underoccupied and certain of their niches are vacant. Gill, as previously noted, believes that there has been a radical late Cenozoic change in Australian environments, including the flora, and that speciational response to it is still active at present. Current negative imbalance may, then, be adaptive lag in occupation of new niches.

Extinction is a continuous and normal part of faunal evolution. It has gone on constantly throughout the history of life as environments changed and as some groups ecologically replaced others. Incomparably more lineages of all geological ages have become extinct than have survived to the present. Pleistocene-Recent extinctions, then, require special explanation only to the extent that they differ from those constantly going on and obvious in the pre-Pleistocene records of Africa and South America, at least. (Also on all the northern continents.) Indeed Pleistocene-Recent extinction in Africa does not seem to have been an extraordinary phenomenon, and if accelerated at all that can be related to some acceleration of environmental change, mainly climatic and floristic but in neither case as radical as on most other continents. In South America the event does seem to have been exceptional, and this can be largely if not wholly ascribed to the fact that in addition to normal or moderately accelerated faunal turnover there was correction of the positive faunal imbalance produced by the incursions from North America. In Australia there was also exceptional extinction and yet there was no positive imbalance by invasion. That can be tentatively explained by climatic and floristic change that was not merely accelerated but revolutionary.

Those broad explanations of the over-all phenomena seem satisfactory as hypotheses, at least. Of course they do not explain explicit instances of extinction, why it was one species and not another that succumbed. The specific causes of extinction are certainly multiple, complex, and subtle in most instances, and often impossible to determine from fossils, as when involving infection or behavior (e.g., Gill, 1955). One can perhaps go one step further, still on a statistical and not individual basis, by observing what categories of animals were most liable to late Cenozoic extinction. Throughout the world, a higher percentage of large mammals, and particularly of large herbivores, became extinct. That is not to say that all large mammals became extinct or that all that became extinct were large, but only that the percentage of extinction was higher for large mammals. That oft-noticed fact has not been satisfactorily explained, but the most obvious hypothesis is that it is correlated with late Cenozoic floristic changes. Such changes would affect herbivores primarily, and large herbivores more than small. Any extinctions on that basis would set up chain reactions first among predators and eventually through the whole fauna. This effect is, again, least noticeable in Africa. There, although many early to middle Pleistocene giants did become extinct, a notable proportion of them have survived. In South America and Australia, practically all the larger Pleistocene mammals became extinct, and neither continent now has herbivores nearly as large as some of those in every other faunal region.

## CONVERGENCE

The phenomena of convergence are shown particularly well and on a grand scale by the southern mammalian faunas. In this respect they richly exemplify the potentialities and limitations of adaptive evolution in general. The three southern continents have many ecological zones and niches that are similar or even virtually identical. Adaptive occupation of those similar ecologies has been independent among the three continents and also partly (Africa), largely (South America), or almost wholly (Australia) independent from similar events on the northern continents. The result has been the evolution of many ecological vicars, which commonly but in extremely varying degrees have convergent functional and anatomical characteristics. The extent to which such convergence has occurred depends on complex interplay of a number of different evolutionary factors, especially:

1. *Basic functional morphological resemblance of stocks peopling the different continents.* For example, the most primitive didelphoid-dasyuroid marsupials were functionally similar to the most primitive insectivorelike-carnivorelike placentals, although genetically distinct from them. That is a factor in the high degree of convergence between marsupial carnivores (separately) in Australia and South America and placental carnivores in Africa (and the north). On the other hand, primitive marsupial herbivores (Australia only) were already functionally quite different from primitive placental ungulates (South America, Africa, and the north), and the degree of later convergence is slight or almost nil.

2. *The particular functions or combinations of functions involved in the ecological similarities.* For example, marsupial "moles" (Australian marsupials) and golden "moles" (African insectivores) are similar in habitats, locomotion, and food, and they are strongly convergent. Tuco-tucos (South American rodents) are similar in habitat, but less so in locomotion and dissimilar in food, and they are only slightly convergent toward the other two. In these examples, as in all, ancestral structural-functional resemblances and differences are also involved. The fairy armadillo (*Chlamyphorus*) of South America is also molelike, but its ancestral dasypod peculiarities have sharply limited the convergence.

3. *Potentialities, structural and genetic, for alternative adaptations serving similar functional ends.* For example, macropids in Australia have adaptations for grazing and browsing and for defense by rapid flight, as do ecologically analogous ungulates in South America, Africa, and elsewhere, but the adaptations are alternative (in that sense opportunistic) and not convergent. (That macropid saltatory bipedalism was an innate tendency simply not selected against seems to be both nonexplanatory and incredible; its defensive and ground-covering powers were surely subject to

strong positive selection, which took this direction because of the ancestral structure and the genetic variants available for that selective action.)

4. *The degree of genetic relationship*. This involves both ancestral structural resemblance and similarity, to some extent homology, of genetic variation available for adaptive selection. This is always involved in some degree, since all mammals do have structural and genetic resemblances, but at one end of the spectrum it may have practically no closer bearing on convergence and at the other it may be the dominant factor, in which case one can speak rather of parallelism than of convergence. The close resemblance of South American caviomorph rodents and ceboid primates with certain African rodents and primates is probably as much parallelism as convergence: they had different immediate ancestors in North America and Eurasia, respectively, but those ancestors were (in each case) almost certainly themselves closely related. The common condylarth ancestral pool also introduces an element of parallelism, although less than in the preceding example, in the numerous and varied convergences of native ungulates in South America, Africa, and the northern continents.

Most cases of convergence involve two, three, or all of these factors simultaneously. Convergence has occurred at all taxonomic levels, from orders downward, and to all degrees, from so great as to have been formerly mistaken for close genetic affinity by able taxonomists (dasyuroids-borhyaenoids; litopterns-horses, etc.) to virtually none. It must further be remembered that convergence is by no means a universal phenomenon, even among the mammals of the southern continents which do provide so many striking examples. Some adaptations simply have appeared in some places and not in others where they would nevertheless be quite possible as far as the environment is concerned, e.g., gliding arboreal herbivores repeatedly in quite different groups in Australia, Africa, Eurasia, and North America but not in South America. In other cases even identical aspects of environments have been parceled out into quite different niches, with no convergence of the animals adapted to them. Mammals feed on acacias in both Africa and

Australia, but no Australian mammal is even remotely convergent toward giraffes!

## REFERENCES


* Bigalke, R. C. 1963. The Living Mammals of Africa. *Proceedings of the XVI International Congress of Zoology,* **4:** 52–55.

Burt, W. H. 1949. Present Distribution and Affinities of Mexican Mammals. *Ann. Assoc. Amer. Geographers,* **39:** 211–218.

* Cooke, H. B. S. 1963. African Mammals in the Fossil Record. *Proceedings of the XVI International Congress of Zoology,* **4:** 46–51.

Cox, A., and R. R. Doell. 1960. Review of Paleomagnetism. *Bull. Geol. Soc. Amer.* **71:** 645–768.

Gill, E. D. 1955. The Problem of Extinction with Special Reference to Australian Marsupials. *Evolution,* **9:** 87–92.

———. 1961. The Climates of Gondwanaland in Kainozoic Times. In *Descriptive Paleoclimatology,* A. E. M. Nairn, Ed., Ch. XIV: 332–353. Interscience Publishers, New York and London.

* Hershkovitz, P. 1963. Recent Mammals of South America. *Proceedings of the XVI International Congress of Zoology,* **4:** 40–45.

Jenks, W. F. (ed.) 1956. *Handbook of South American Geology.* Geol. Soc. Amer., Mem. 65.

* Keast, A. 1963. Introduction to Special Symposium. *Proceedings of the XVI International Congress of Zoology,* **4:** 37–39.

* ———. 1963 The Mammal Fauna of Australia. *Proceedings of the XVI International Congress of Zoology,* **4:** 56–62.

Kummel, B. 1961. *History of the Earth.* W. H. Freeman and Co., San Francisco and London.

* Patterson, B., and R. Pascual. 1963. The Extinct Land Mammals of South America. *Proceedings of the XVI International Congress of Zoology,* Program Vol., Appendix, 138–148.

Simpson, G. G. 1943. Mammals and the Nature of Continents. *Amer. Jour. Sci.,* **241:** 1–31.

———. 1950. History of the Fauna of Latin America. *Amer. Scientist,* **38:** 361–389.

———. 1953. *Evolution and Geography*. Oregon State System of Higher Education, Eugene.

———. 1961 a. The Supposed Pliocene Pebas Beds of the Upper Juruá River, Brazil. *Jour. Paleo.*, **35**: 620–624.

———. 1961 b. Historical Zoogeography of Australian Mammals. *Evolution*, **15**: 431–446.

* Abstracts from the symposium referred to on p. 211.

# INDEX